BE COOL
DESPITE
GLOBAL WARMING

John H. Hacker, P.E.

John H. Hacker

I-FORM INK PUBLISHING

Published by
I-Form Ink Publishing
A division of Insu-Form, Incorporated, a California Corporation
41-921 Beacon Hill, Suite A
Palm Desert, California 92211

Visit us on the Web! www.i-form-ink.com
E-mail: john@i-form-ink.com
Copies of this book are available at Amazon.com

Library of Congress Control Number: 2006910887
ISBN: 978-0-9763274-5-5

Printed in the United States of America by Morris Publishing
3212 East Highway 30
Kearney, NE 68847
1-800-650-7888

Cover by Jonathan Gorges
Illustrations by John H. Hacker
Edited by Julie A. Gorges

TABLE OF CONTENTS

Chapter One

IS GLOBAL WARMING BY GREENHOUSE GASES A REAL DANGER?

The summer of 2006 was one of the hottest ever recorded and we can expect it to get hotter. The extra heat, which cannot escape, is beginning to change the global patterns of climate to which we are accustomed and to which we have adapted over the last several thousand years.

"Because of our new technological power and our growing numbers, we now must pay careful attention to the consequences of what we are doing to the Earth -- especially to the most vulnerable part of the Earth's environment, the very thin layer of air clinging near to the surface of the planet, that we are now so carelessly filling with gaseous wastes that we are actually altering the relationship between the Earth and the Sun -- by trapping more solar radiation under this growing blanket of pollution that envelops the entire world." Remarks at the United Nations Committee on Climate Change by Vice President Al Gore on December 8, 1997.

The United States with about 4.5 percent of the world's population now produces about 18 percent of the greenhouse gas emissions, the most of any nation on earth. In 2004, a nationwide poll by the Global Strategy Group found that 70 percent of Americans consider global warming a "very serious" or "somewhat serious" problem.

Since statistics show that domestic energy use makes up approximately a quarter of all the country's carbon dioxide emissions, building energy efficient homes has become an important way to take responsibility for any adverse environmental impact resulting from our use of energy.

In addition to preventing unnecessary pollution, energy efficient homes can cut energy costs by over 40 percent in most affordable housing, according to the United States Department of Energy. Other benefits include a healthy indoor environment, reduced noise, greater fire safety and improved building durability.

With electricity becoming more expensive along with the price of natural gas and the possibility that blackouts may occur if we do not conserve energy, what are the alternatives? What can we do to make our homes more energy efficient, and stay cooler?

Perhaps you're aware of some ways to make a house more energy efficient, such as increasing insulation and sealing air leaks. However, this book also addresses the importance of using alternate building materials like steel framing and slab edge insulation, as well as lesser known methods such as using radiant barriers in the attic. Before we begin, however, let's consider why it's so important to consider using these alternatives to prevent cutting down old growth forests for lumber.

WHY DESTROYING OUR FORESTS IS DESTROYING OUR FUTURE

According to experts, it takes about one acre of forest (30 trees) to clean the air of carbon dioxide for each person; therefore, we need to protect and expand our forests. Since it takes up to 50 trees to build a home out of wood, shouldn't we consider alternate building materials?

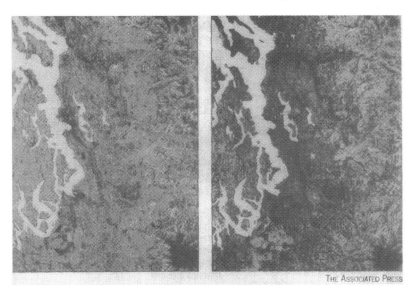

THE ASSOCIATED PRESS

SEATTLE AREA 1972   SEATTLE AREA 1996

The above satellite photos of the Seattle Area; released by American Forest, shows how much of the surrounding area has been clear cut.

The dark areas have less than 20 percent tree cover as compared to the gray areas with over 50 percent.

The United States Energy Information Administration (EIA) released a report on October 25, 1997 titled Emissions of Greenhouse Gases in the United States, which stated, "From a global warming perspective, the most important land use issues are those related to forest creation and destruction. Forests and forest soils remove and store large amounts of carbon from the atmosphere."

As noted in the Executive Summary of this report, of the trace gases, "carbon dioxide is the largest single contributor to global warming, responsible for 85 percent of United States global warming potential (GWP)-weighted emissions of greenhouse gases. Thus, from a global warming perspective, the most important modifications in land use are those that significantly affect the carbon budget."

The report added: "The most important changes in land use are those that increase or reduce forest land. United States forests removed a net 123 million metric tons of carbon in 1990, including the net 12 million metric tons sequestered in wood products and the net 15 million metric tons sequestered in land filled wood product waste. This quantity would offset approximately nine percent of the 1,430 million metric tons of carbon emitted by the United States in 1994 from the burning of fossil fuels."

Trees and branches, and other decaying biomass all add carbon to the soil as they decompose, even though most carbon is released to the atmosphere. More importantly, a large amount of carbon is added underground to the soil as roots die and slough off. The older a forest becomes without major perturbations (such as intense fires or conversion to crop land), the more carbon is stored in the soil. Clearing forest land sets the stage for large-scale losses of carbon to the atmosphere.

An Associated Press article quoted from a report prepared by The World Wildlife Fund for Nature, released on December 12, 1997 in London, stated, "As we destroy forests, we are destroying our insurance for the future." The report also criticized the United States for using the risk of fire as an excuse for felling old-growth forest rich in wildlife to subsidize the logging industry.

In an article on the same day, the Associated Press quoted Common Cause's president, Ann McBride: "What happened to the road credit program in 1997 was an outrageous demonstration of the power of big money on public policy. Timber interests tripled their soft-money spending in 1995-96, a move that seemed to help them gain leverage with Congress despite the environmental concerns of the overwhelming majority of Americans." According to the article, the lumber industry has made more than 8 million dollars in contributions since 1991 including a significant increase the past two years in "soft money" checks.

The lumber industry also reported spending $2.9 million in lobbying expenses for the first six months of 1997.

What has been the effect of these contributions and lobbying according to these watchdog groups? The government has spent tax payer's money subsidizing the lumber companies to cut trees in our National Forests. When we consider that over ten million homes have been built using lumber since 1997, some 400 million trees have been cut to build these homes. The forests must be protected.

Environmental groups sued the United States Forest Service after it reversed President Clinton's "Road less Rule" of January 2001, prohibiting commercial logging, mining and other development on 58.5 million acres of national forests. When a Federal Judge recently reinstated the ban, overturning a Bush administration rule that could have cleared the way for more commercial activity in national forests, the timber industry denounced the decision using the same argument, saying it would leave road less areas vulnerable to catastrophic wildfires.

MAKING THE BEST USES OF RESOURCES

There are other alternatives to cutting down old growth forests for building houses.

In fact, surveys have demonstrated that builders are looking for more product innovation, including steel framing, structural insulated panels, new concrete products and energy-efficient products. Let's discuss a few of these alternatives.

Steel Framing

Why should you consider steel framing? Look at the following facts:

- While it takes 25 to 50 trees to frame an average house of wood, it takes less than six junked cars to frame in steel.

- Each year, in the United States, over 1.3 million residential structures are built, which means each year over 50 million trees are cut from forests in the United States and Canada for new residential construction alone.

- Steel is a recyclable material and can be reused indefinitely. If a steel-framed house is torn down, the steel can be reused, while wood from houses built with lumber are generally taken to a land fill.

- Other advantages: steel won't warp, bow, rot or fall victim to termites; steel has superior fire ratings; homes are more hurricane- and typhoon-resistant; the cost of steel is stable in comparison with volatile wood prices.

The tools used to frame a steel frame are basically the same as in any other type of construction except for the following items, which can be obtained at a reasonable cost at most building supply stores:

1. A chop saw with metal cutting blades
2. Vice grips designed for metal fabrication
3. Tin snips to trim the metal
4. Power screw guns
5. Hole punch

Steel framed homes have one disadvantage: the energy loss that occurs because of greater heat transfer and thermal bridging. However, you *can* compensate for the energy lost through steel construction. With over 50 years experience in designing energy efficient steel buildings, I have seen this fact proven over and over again.

Chapters Eight through Thirteen details how to build an award winning house using steel stud construction. To compensate for the heat transfer in steel, I'll show you how to use thermal breaks in the construction and still provide an energy efficient house. If preferred, you can also build the house using wood stud construction and apply the suggestions for energy savings.

Chapter Fourteen details how to build a steel framed house with foamed cement exterior walls made from recycled waste materials.

Alternative wood products

Wood products are available that do not come from public woodlands, but are planted on managed timberlands.

These products can be manufactured from fast-growing species, relatively small trees, and species that are otherwise unfit for standard veneer plywood or lumber. The production process utilizes a maximum amount of wood fiber from each tree that is harvested, thereby providing for efficient utilization of wood fiber resource.

One of these alternative materials is Oriented Strand Board (OSB) and wafer board, which is engineered, mat-formed panel products made of strands, flakes or wafers sliced from small diameter, round wood logs and bonded with an exterior-type binder under heat and pressure.

Another material you may want to consider is laminated veneer lumber (LVL), an engineered wood product created by layering dried and graded wood veneers with waterproof adhesive into blocks of material known as billets. Cured in a heated press, LVL is typically available in various thicknesses and widths and is easily worked in the field using conventional construction tools. LVL is also known as structural composite lumber (SCL).

I-joists are another product made of structural composite lumber which allows the manufacturer to make the most efficient use of wood fiber resources while producing products that consistently perform to known standards.

To their credit, some retailers such as Home Depot and Lowe's have made it their policy not to sell wood products that come from old growth forests.

CHAPTER TWO

BASIC WAYS TO MAKE A HOUSE COOLER

The following graph demonstrates the energy losses in a typical 1,400 square foot house with a calculated heat loss or gain of as much as 30,000 btuh (British thermal units per hour) during extreme cold or heat occurrences.

Items that can be improved are floors, ducts, and infiltration, which contribute to the major heat loss and gain in an ordinary house. In this calculation, it was assumed that existing windows were dual-pane, the walls were insulated a minimum of R-11 and the ceiling insulated with R-38.

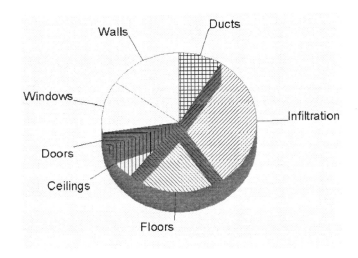

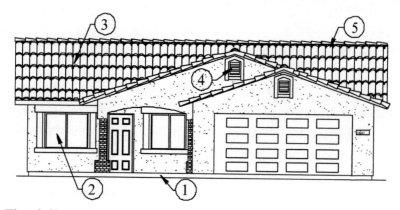

The following are some basic ways you can improve the

AREAS OF IMPROVEMENT IN A TYPICAL HOUSE

energy efficiency in your house. Details of these improvements are in chapters as noted.

1.   SLAB EDGE INSULATION

Slab edge insulation makes a tremendous difference in cooling your house. When combined with hard surfaces on the inside floors of your house, it provides a heat sink to allow excess heat to escape into the cooler ground under the slab. Estimated savings are up to 4000 btu per hour in cooling and heating costs. Materials should cost about $1 a lineal foot and can be a do-it-yourself project. (See Chapter Four.)

2. SOLAR WINDOW SCREENS AND WINDOW
    TINTING

Solar screens block up to 90 percent of the heat
trying to enter through your windows and 100
percent of UV (ultra-violet light) radiation. Simply
replace your existing screens with solar screens or
install retractable screens on the inside of the
windows and sliding door jams. Window tinting
material will cost about $2.50 per square foot. (See
Chapter Five.)

3. DUCT TESTING AND INSULATION

Testing your ducts for leakage and sealing the
leaks is a cost effective measure. Fixing leaking
ducts will lower your air-conditioning costs and
help maintain a comfortable home. Another cost-
effective measure is adding insulation to the ducts.
Most homes have ducts that are insulated with R-4
insulation, even though the ceiling may be
insulated with R-38. If you get a blast of hot air
when you first turn on your air conditioner,
insulate your ducts with another layer of R-11
insulation. This is a simple do-it-yourself job and
the material is not expensive.

4.   ATTIC EXHAUST VENTILATION

Power vents actively remove heat from your attic. These vents are thermostatically controlled and fan driven. A 1,600 cfm (cubit feet per minute) fan is adequate for up to 1,500 square feet of attic space. Typically fans reduce cooling costs by $20 to $40 per summer month. A gable end fan unit costs about $60 and a roof mount less than $100 plus installation and wiring. (See Chapter Six.)

5.   RADIANT BARRIER

A radiant barrier reflects heat away from the attic when applied to the underside of the roof rafters and allows less than 20 percent of the sun's radiant heat to enter your attic (emissivity of .24). Installation of a radiant barrier can reduce cooling costs by $15 to $30 per summer month. The material costs about 50 cents per square foot and can be a do-it-yourself job. Radiant barrier material can also be applied over the top of the attic insulation. Since it could function as a vapor barrier, use perforated material for this application. Dust can also accumulate on the surface and inhibit performance. When the material is placed flat on the attic insulation, it can also be punctured or torn during any service work that may have to be done in the attic. (See Chapter Five.)

Some additional common sense tips:

- Set your thermostat lower in the winter and higher in the summer. Seventy-eight degrees is now recommended to save energy during heat waves. Install a programmable thermostat that is compatible with your cooling system.

- In older homes, a great deal of energy is lost due to gaps and openings around windows and doors. Use a caulking gun to fill in these gaps. Add gaskets to all your exterior wall plugs.

- Add insulation to your ceiling. If you have a flat roof, consider adding polyurethane foam to the roof, which decreases your energy expense by limiting the amount of heat lost through your roof. This method will prevent nearly 100 percent of heat loss through air infiltration with the first one-fourth of an inch of applied foam. Stopping the air, moisture, and heat from leaving the comfortable confines of your home or business directly converts into energy savings. Studies show potential energy savings of 20 to 40 percent. Each inch adds an R-6 insulating value. Other benefits, such as reduced sound and odor penetration, may also be of value.

- Use compact fluorescent light bulbs.

- Air dry dishes instead of using the dishwasher's drying cycle.

- Turn off your computer and monitor when not in use.

- Plug home electronics such as TVs and DVD players into power strips; turn off the power strips when the equipment is not in use.

- Refrigerators older than 1990 can use three times as much electricity as newer ones.

- Install glass doors on your fireplace opening. Or if you do not use it, consider sealing the chimney. A great deal of conditioned air can escape up an open chimney.

- Install ceiling fans in as many rooms as possible.

- Install an evaporative cooler to use when the humidity is low or when no one is present in the house. The evaporative cooler should have back flow dampers on the registers and one Up-Dux™ return to the attic for every 1000 cfm. This will eliminate the need to open windows when the unit is running. Although evaporative coolers are energy efficient, be aware that this equipment will only lower the temperature by about 20 degrees.

- Old, drafty, single-pane windows are often responsible for about 40-50 percent of the heat lost or gained. Air tight windows are essential. If you have older windows consider installing vinyl replacement dual pane windows which can increase the energy efficiency of your home by two to three times.

Chapter Three

HEAT TRANSFER AND WHAT YOU NEED TO KNOW ABOUT R-VALUES

The transfer of heat takes place by one or more of three methods – conduction, convection, and radiation. These natural forces work separately and together in transferring heat between objects. Chapters Four, Five and Six discuss how to prevent losses from these three methods.

To illustrate the effect of convection losses in energy efficiency, it's important to realize that the insulating value of most insulating materials is provided by trapping air and preventing air movement. For example, fur in animals provides insulation by trapping air, which is why people wear wool sweaters. When the wind blows, it creates a "wind chill factor," effectively reducing the insulating value by convection.

Heat seeks a balance with surrounding areas. Therefore, heat moves from the inside to the outside during the winter and from the outside to the inside during the hot summer. Heat can also occur between two mediums, moving from the warmer medium to the cooler medium. Therefore, heat not only flows through the assembly from inside to outside of the building envelope, but also moves from the center of the insulated cavity to the framing members.

THE TRUTH ABOUT R-VALUES

Resistance ® is the measure of a material's ability to resist the flow of heat through it, so the higher the R-value of a material, the greater its resistance to heat flow.

Another measure of heat flow through materials is known as U, which refers to the ability of an entire built-up section, such as the wall or window section, to permit the flow of heat. The U-value is important in calculating heat loss and when comparing window units. U is the inverse of the total R, so, the lower the U-value, the higher the insulating value.

In general, the public – and many architects and builders - assume a higher R-value means better performance. However, that's not always the case. Although R-value is a legitimate laboratory measurement of thermal resistance, it doesn't necessarily predict performance.

The R-value insulating rating mechanism was developed by the United States Federal Trade Commission to help put an end to false and misleading claims about insulation that once existed. While the R-value measurement gives important information about thermal resistance in laboratory settings, the R-value changes with extreme temperature differences.

The performance under specific conditions is called effective R-value. Since information on effective R-value performance for fiberglass products is not required by law, you won't see anything about it on insulation packaging or in their specifications charts.

This is important because the effective R-values of fiberglass and other insulating materials change under very cold or hot temperatures. Studies at the Oak Ridge National Laboratory have shown that at 20 degrees below zero, fiberglass can lose as much as half its R-value, while solid fill insulation such as cellulose or foamed concrete products perform at a higher R-value at 20 degrees below zero than at 70 degrees.

In 1990, the University of Colorado studied the energy conservation efficiency of two test buildings that differed only in the insulation installed. One building installed wet-spray cellulose in the walls and loose-fill cellulose in the ceiling; the other building used standard fiberglass insulation. The results were interesting. The solid filled cellulose walled building was not only 36 percent tighter than the fiberglass building, but used 26.4 percent less energy to heat than the fiberglass.

If you are planning to construct a new building, I would highly recommend that you consider using cellulose wall insulation, which is recycled newspaper. Another good product to use as insulation is foamed cement blocks which also is made from a waste material, fly ash.

CHAPTER FOUR

PREVENTING CONDUCTION

Conduction is the transfer of heat through a solid material or from one material to another when surfaces are touching, from the warmest part to the coolest part.

Dense materials such as concrete, metal, or glass conduct heat more rapidly than porous materials such as wood or fiber products. Any material will conduct some heat when a temperature difference exists.

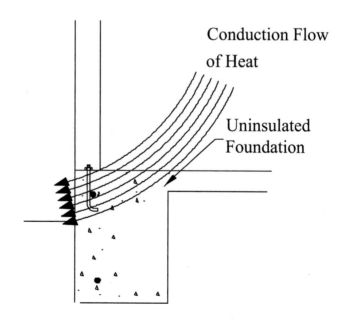

Conduction Flow of Heat

Uninsulated Foundation

HEAT TRANSFER THROUGH THE FOOTING

Conductive losses are most prevalent when the same material is exposed to both inside and outside temperatures. Areas of particular concern include built-up headers, studs, corners, window sash and glazing, plates and band joists, and concrete floors.

The conduction of heat through building materials is a major source of heat loss or gain.

SLAB EDGE INSULATION

An insulated slab makes a tremendous difference. This is an important energy saving element often ignored.

Concrete slab floors lose heat to the earth and foundation walls by conduction and through exposed edges by convection and radiation. Because the distance the heat travels to the colder or hotter ground is further from the center, the greatest heat loss or gain is at the edge of the slab.

One meter of exposed un-insulated slab edge loses or gains as much heat as several square meters of insulated wall area, which is a significant amount.

Insulating the slab reduces heat loss or gain and maintains warmer or cooler floor surface temperatures inside.

The figures below are based on a Manual J energy calculation program. As you can see, the energy savings from an insulated slab are substantial. In a standard sized house, savings can be a loss or gain of about 4000 btuh.

HEAT LOSS OR GAIN IN A SAMPLE HOUSE WITH R-7 SLAB EDGE INSULATION

Component	btuh/Sq. Ft.	Btuh	% of btuh
Floors	17.3	2005	12.3

HEAT LOSS OR GAIN IN A SAMPLE HOUSE WITHOUT SLAB EDGE INSULATION

Component	btuh/Sq. Ft.	btuh	% of btuh
Floors	51.8	6015	20.7

In very cold climates, slab edge insulation also prevents condensation and frost formation along the inside edge of the floor.

For more than 25 years in Europe, frost-protected shallow foundations (FPSF) have been used in hundreds of thousands homes around the foundation perimeter. Insulation around the foundation perimeter conserves and redirects heat loss through the building slab toward the soil beneath the building foundation. At the same time, geothermal heat resources are directed toward the foundation, resulting in an elevated frost depth around the building. In cold areas of the country, this method eliminates the need for basements and deep foundations with crawl spaces that permit infiltration into the home.

In areas requiring deep footing placement to provide frost protection, FPSFs may allow a foundation depth as shallow as 12 inches or 305 millimeters and can provide immediate savings due to reduced material costs.

The follow details have been used to insulate slabs in the Southern California area and have given good results in maintaining cool homes:

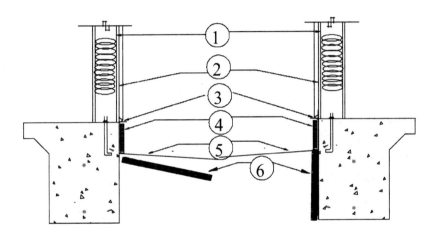

SLAB EDGE INSULATION   ALTERNATE DETAIL

1. Existing wall insulation
2. Existing wall exterior finish
3. Existing weep screed for stucco walls
4. One inch extruded Styrofoam
5. Existing ground, leave six inches below finish floor
6. Install one inch extruded Styrofoam in ground, either out 12 inches from the foundation in a shallow trench (first detail) or in a vertical trench 12 inches deep alongside the foundation.

Installation Instructions:

1. Buy 4' x 8' x 1" sheets of extruded polystyrene rigid insulation. The price at Home Depot, at the time of this writing was about $10 a sheet.

2. Use a table saw with a metal cutting carborundum blade, which makes a cleaner cut and does not tend to tear the foam like a wood cutting blade. Cut the sheet into three 4-inch wide strips and three 12-inch wide strips. One sheet should provide the insulation for 24 lineal feet of slab insulation.

3. Dig a trench around the foundation. This trench may be shallow (1 to 4 inches deep) out 12 inches from the foundation. An alternate is to dig a vertical trench 12 inches deep alongside the foundation as shown in the illustration above.

4. Glue the 4-inch strip of rigid insulation onto the side of the exposed concrete foundation. Be sure to allow a gap at the top for water to exit from the weep screeds.

5. Coat the 4-inch insulation with EIFS stucco or an elastomeric stucco finish to protect the insulation.

6. Install the 12-inch insulation in the ground and backfill.

Commercial firms will install urethane sprayed-on foam, applied in a 1 to 2 inch thickness, depending on the house siding gap. The ground next to the foundation is dug out 12 inches deep and 12 inches wide around the house. An acrylic or urethane coating is applied over the foam.

If there is an existing concrete slab adjacent to the foundation, it is not necessary to insulate the slab. Nor is it necessary to insulate the garage footings.

In the desert, when workmen enter houses with slab edge insulation and the floor is still uncovered concrete, they often comment how the house is cooler compared to outside temperatures.

USE HARD SURFACES ON FLOORS INSTEAD OF CARPET

Another way to use conduction to remove heat is by using hard surfaces, such as tile or laminated wood flooring, instead of carpet.

Replacing the carpet with a hard surface will help you benefit from the "heat sink effect." Basically this means your floor will dissipate the heat from inside your home into the ground underneath the slab.

Twelve inches into the ground can be as much as 30 degrees cooler than the temperature in a house. During hot summers in the desert, when temperatures can reach 120 degrees, conduction can be used to keep a house as much as 20 degrees cooler without air conditioning.

To illustrate, in 1987 my office provided an energy consultation for a client who owned an expensive house in Rancho Mirage, in the California desert. As we recommended, he used slab edge insulation and tile throughout the house. The home was only used in the winter as a vacation house but was filled with expensive antiques. The following summer, a power outage lasted several days. The owner was concerned and asked a friend to check on the house. Although the temperature was 115 degrees outside, the friend reported the temperature was about 90 degrees inside the house with no air conditioning.

If you prefer not to use tile, laminated flooring is cheaper than its hardwood counterpart and is protected by a thin layer of laminate, usually made of aluminum oxide, which is resistant to scratches, burns, chipping, and dents, and most importantly, suitable for foot traffic.

The pattern layer is made from a screen that is created to replicate the look of real wood or tile floors. The core layer is created using High Density Fiber (HDF) which is moisture resistant and durable. The HDF layer is very difficult to scratch or stain and houses the locking system, which aids in the installation of the floor. In addition, HDF is a dense material and provides a good convection of the heat to the concrete.

USE AN EVAPORATIVE COOLER TO STORE COOLNESS IN THE SLAB

In the past, many people opened windows to take advantage of the cool night air. With the increase of crime, however, families often feel safer if the house is locked up. Nonetheless, using this free cool air is still an important item because the outside temperature lowers significantly in the early morning hours.

During the construction of an energy efficient house, attention is paid to eliminating convection heat by making the house almost air tight. Unfortunately, this practice also traps stale air in the house. How can you counteract this problem and import fresh air into the house?

One way is to use an air to air heat exchanger. These units remove the heat or cooling from the expelled air and introduce it into the return outside air, but this equipment can be expensive and uses energy.

In my award winning house, I installed a 4000 cfm evaporative cooler along with UP-Dux registers that open when the evaporative cooler is operating. The air is expelled into the attic and out the attic vents. A time clock/thermostat turns on the evaporative cooler when the cooler outside air is available. The equipment can be set to operate without water to the pads if humidity is high. This provides a complete change of air each day and eliminates air tight house syndrome.

The cooler air will also lower the temperature of the slab floor and stores the coolness for the next day. In some climates, this alternative is enough to provide daytime cooling.

CHAPTER FIVE

COMBATING RADIATION WITH PROPER WINDOWS, LANDSCAPING, RADIANT BARRIERS AND WHITE ROOFS

Radiant heat from the sun, which is 93,000,000 miles away, does not necessarily warm the air. Consequently, the air temperature may be 80 degrees or less, while a dark colored roof surface temperature may be 150 degrees or higher.

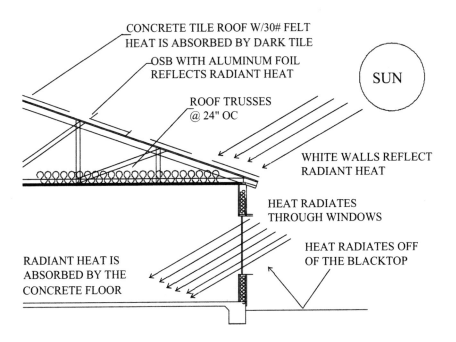

Radiation takes place without a medium. Radiant energy directly transfers heat through space by electromagnetic waves, traveling at the speed of light until absorbed by a solid or reflected. After absorbing heat, all objects radiate heat, assuming the object is hotter than the air surrounding it. The higher the temperature of the object, the greater the quantity of heat radiated. The amount of radiant heat depends, not only on the temperature of the radiating object, but also on the extent and nature of its surface.

A rough, dark surface, for example, radiates more heat than a smooth, bright surface at the same temperature. Building materials emit radiant heat in all directions to any surface at a lower temperature. Windows and glazing contribute significantly to radiant heat gain or loss.

WINDOWS AND DOORS

Windows are a significant source of heat gain. The ideal window is dual pane, low-e glass with vinyl frames filled with argon gas. The ideal door is a self hung hollow metal-insulated door with a R-value of 6; the ideal garage door is an insulated foam-core R-5.2 door.

If your house has single pane windows with metal frames you may want to replace them with dual panes. If doors have gaps at the sides, it would be well to replace them as well.

What if your house already has dual pane windows? We'll consider other ways to prevent convection heat from entering the house.

WINDOW TINTING

Do-it-yourself film is available for those who want to save money. Manufacturers claim these films reduce heat gain by 50 percent and glare by 62 percent.

Window tinting is available in a neutral colored film perfect for all applications. The tinting is a non-fade 100 percent metalized film that reaps more than 65 percent fade reduction on your home furnishings. Easily installed by one person, films are available in 30 and 60 inch widths by 20, 30, 50, 80, and 100 foot rolls.

SOLAR SCREENS

Solar screens are a unique woven mesh that can block up to 80 percent of the sun's hot rays before entering through windows. In addition, these screens work as an effective insect screen with a tighter weave.

The material has a solar rating of 80 to 93 percent, depending on the color. The solar fabric also allows air to pass through.

These screens are an excellent choice for windows facing west or east. Solar screens are also available as double door retractable screens for sliding glass doors. Most sliding glass doors have one fixed panel which does not affect the installation since it covers the entire opening. The screen is virtually invisible when not in use and is extended only when closed to keep the sun out or to allow cool breezes to come in.

These screens are available as do-it-yourself projects and the retractable screen doors can be installed on the outside of the building in the weather or inside the door jamb (1 ½ inch minimum depth is required).

A wide variety of styles and types of retractable screens are available including simple pull-down models and models with a hand crank. Deluxe models have motors, some come with remote controls.

LANDSCAPING

If your site permits, one of the easiest ways to prevent thermal radiation on the windows is to plant trees to provide shade on west, east and south-facing windows. In cooler climates, deciduous trees should be used on the west, east, and south sides of a house to take advantage of heat gain from the sun during winter.

Plant evergreen trees for windbreaks on the north side of the house. As an additional benefit, each tree as it matures absorbs carbon dioxide.

Minimize heat-absorbent material like asphalt, especially near the house.

RADIANT BARRIERS IN THE ATTIC

A Radiant Barrier is an aluminum foil typically installed on the bottom of roof rafters. This is a job that can be done easily with a staple gun.

The surface of aluminum has the ability, not to absorb, but to reflect 95 percent of the infrared rays. Since aluminum foil has such a low mass to air ratio, very little conduction can take place since only 5 percent of the rays are absorbed.

Try this experiment: Hold a square of aluminum foil close to your face without touching it. Soon you'll feel the warmth of your own infrared rays bouncing back from the surface of the foil.

How does this work? The emissivity of heat radiation of the surface of your face is 99 percent while the absorption of aluminum is only 3 percent. Therefore, the aluminum foil sends back 96 percent of the rays. The result is that you feel the warmth of your face reflected.

Walls and roofs are built with internal air spaces to retard heat flow by conduction. Conduction and convection through these air spaces combined represent only 20 to 35 percent of the heat passed through. Sixty-five to 80 percent of heat that passes from a warm wall to a colder wall or through a ventilated attic does so by radiation.

The value of air spaces as thermal insulation must include the character of the enclosing surfaces. The surfaces greatly affect the amount of energy transferred by radiation, depending on the material's absorptivity and emissivity and are the only way of modifying the total heat transferred across a given space. The importance of radiation cannot be overlooked in problems involving ordinary room temperatures.

The following data, provided by The Tennessee Valley Authority, Chattanooga, Tennessee on Performance Testing of Radiant Barriers, demonstrates the economic savings possible for a typical home.

According to the study, all Radiant Barrier configurations yielded sizable percent savings (17 percent, based on Energy Star Evaluation) and significant reductions in summer attic heat transfer compared to the non-Radiant Barrier case. As the ambient temperature increased, the savings increased.

The Radiant Barrier on top was the best summer performer. It consistently showed heat flux reductions compared to the non-Radiant Barrier case of about 40 percent for almost all ambient temperatures and even showed savings (17 percent) during mild temperature and night summer conditions.

The Radiant Barrier configurations provide statistically significant reductions in winter attic heat fluxes in many, but not all, situations. The savings during night hours and below 35 degree conditions - when heating loads are the highest - are usually sizable (from 6 to 23 percent) and the differences between the Radiant Barrier configurations and the non-Radiant Barrier case are often significant.

There are many different types, grades, and qualities of aluminum foil insulation designed for various application. Some companies have a three-layer product with an outer layer of foil and a center layer of vinyl and another outer layer of aluminum that is more durable and does not tear as easily as some brands. Use only foil specifically designed for attic installation.

WHITE ROOFS

The California Energy Commission now requires that new flat roofs be white and in 2008 will require new sloped roofs to be colors proven to reflect, at a minimum, half as much heat as white roofs.

A white roof can save a kilowatt hour of electricity every hour on a hot afternoon. A kilowatt hour currently costs from 12 to 37 cents depending on the amount used, but is expected to rise to more than 50 cents in the near future.

Recently, high energy prices have made elastomeric coatings the most popular alternative to roof replacement. An elastomeric coating can reflect up to 90 percent of heat from the sun. When installed on a hot black roof, a reflective roof coating keeps the roof from absorbing the heat and transmitting it into the building. Virtually any roof type can be restored such as gravel built-up roofing, metal roofing, modified bitumen, polyurethane foam, and smooth built-up roofing.

However, it's only economically feasible to change sloped roof colors when you need to replace the roof. If your house has a flat roof, it is possible to coat the existing surface with a white coating at a reasonable price. Most flat roofs do not have an attic, so this would be an alternate to installing a radiant barrier.

CHAPTER SIX
FIGHTING CONVECTION WITH ATTIC VENTILATION

Convection is the transfer of heat due to the movement of a fluid, typically air or water. Molecules of gas (air) or some liquids (water) become less dense and lighter when heated and rise. As warmer molecules rise, the cooler ones sink to create convection currents.

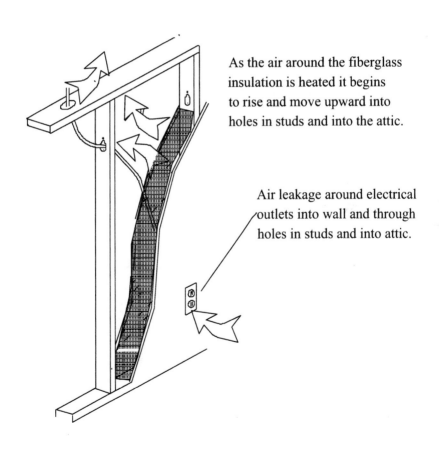

As the air around the fiberglass insulation is heated it begins to rise and move upward into holes in studs and into the attic.

Air leakage around electrical outlets into wall and through holes in studs and into attic.

Convective heat transfer usually works in conjunction with conductive heat transfer. One location air escapes is electrical boxes. Check to see if there are gaps around these boxes and install foam outlet gaskets at each location. These are easy to install and cost about 10 cents each. Check the doors and windows and install weather stripping as necessary.

ATTIC VENTILATION

Attic ventilation can eliminate excessive heat and humidity that builds up in your attic.

The temperature in the attic can exceed 150 degrees during the summer, even if the outside temperature is only 95 to 97 degrees. The cooling load for a home air conditioner depends on the difference in temperature between inside and outside air. Reducing the attic temperature from 150 to 105 degrees will result in a significant reduction of the cooling load. Therefore, you may want to install or have a qualified contractor install some type of power ventilation in the attic.

Be aware that some roof ventilation configurations may require special consideration and recommendations to perform properly. Power fan vents work best when used in a balanced attic ventilation system. This requires the volume of air intake (such as under eave vents) to match or exceed the volume of air exhaust. How much attic ventilation is required to provide temperature and moisture control?

The minimum area of ventilation required in square feet by building codes is the attic area divided by 150.

If your house has gable vents, the installation of a gable end vent is a simple do-it yourself project.

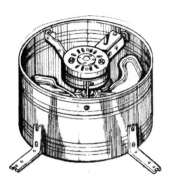

TYPICAL GABLE END VENTILATOR FAN

The ventilator is designed to mount behind existing gable vent louvers. For maximum efficiency, the area of the louver should be greater than the outlet area of the ventilator. The louver will block some of the air flow resulting in some loss in fan output. Metal louvers have more open area than wood louvers and allow more air flow.

Seal off any louver area not covered by the ventilator housing band to prevent air recirculation. You might want to mount the ventilator on a piece of plywood first for best sealing. Allow one square foot of air intake for each 300 cubic feet per minute of ventilator capacity.

To provide the minimum ventilation rate required to move heat during the summer months, it is recommended the fan provide a minimum of one cubic foot per minute for each square foot of attic area. Providing one air change per minute will lower the peak attic temperature to about 101 degrees, using a 95 degree outside air temperature.

CONVECTION LOSSES UP THE CHIMNEY

If you live in an old house you may have a fireplace that was constructed out of masonry. These fireplaces are inefficient for heating homes.

Although sentimental songs describe roasting chestnuts over an open fire, the burning of wood releases carbon dioxide. Even if you only use dead and fallen trees for a roaring fire, think about this: If the tree was allowed to decay naturally on the forest floor, the carbon within would be transmitted into the soil and not the air.

Any smoke that escapes from your wood stove unburned is wasted fuel that sticks in your chimney as creosote and is released as air pollution. In addition, an old or poorly installed wood fireplace results in higher maintenance costs and can cause house fires.

When it's cold outside, the warm air inside the house rises, producing a pressure difference called "the stack effect." The result is that fireplace chimneys can sometimes draw in more cold outside air than can be heated by the fireplace, resulting in a net heat loss.

After chopping the wood, cleaning the chimney and raking out ashes, your old wood fireplace will not only rob more heat from your home than it delivers, but puff smoke into your home on bad weather days.

If you wish to continue using the fireplace, install a fire box. You can keep the beautiful look of your wood burning fireplace with the added cleanliness, energy efficiency and convenience of a gas insert. The insulating characteristics trap the heat in the firebox, allowing it to better radiate heat into your home. Also the gas insert holds heat well after the fireplace is turned off, resulting in greater overall efficiency.

The slant back design and molded blower chamber allows the insert to slide directly into most existing fireplaces. The direct vent, sealed combustion chamber in many units uses 29,600 btu/input; 80 percent AFUE (annual fuel utilization efficiency) rating, about 40 percent or less than a wood burning masonry unit.

The detail below is a natural gas fireplace installed in a model home constructed by the Boys Club. The fireplace is a sealed unit with automatic controls and a blower and does not need electricity to operate, which makes it a good back-up in the event of an electrical blackout.

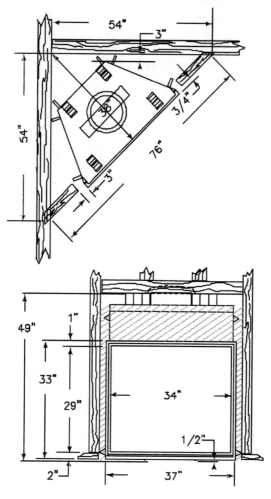

At a minimum, install tight fitting glass doors and keep them closed when the fireplace is not being used.

CHAPTER SEVEN
LOWERING YOUR UTILITY BILLS

We'll begin by helping you understand some of the terms used in utility bills.

BTU

A btu (British Thermal Unit) is the amount of thermal energy required to raise the temperature of one pound of water by one degree Fahrenheit. A simple illustration is that a lighted match will produce about one btu of heat.

The btu content provided below and used in energy calculations reflect the average energy contents for fuels consumed in the United States:

One gallon of gasoline = 124,000 btu

One gallon of diesel fuel = 139,000 btu

One gallon of heating oil = 139,000 btu

One barrel of residual fuel oil = 6,287,000 btu

One cubic foot of natural gas = 1,031 btu

One gallon of propane = 91,000 btu

One short ton of coal = 20,754,000 btu

One kilowatt-hour of electricity = 3,412 btu

Kilowatt-hour (kWh)

The initials kWH stand for the basic unit of electric energy equivalent to one kilowatt used for one hour.

For example, ten 100 watt light bulbs will use one kWh in one hour (10 bulbs x 100 watts x one hour = 1000 watt-hours, or one kWh). In the case of a resistance type appliance, such as a toaster or portable heater, one kWh is equal to 3,413 btu.

If you are heating your home with a heat pump, which utilizes the existing heat in the air, you'll be producing more btu per kWh.

Therm

This term refers to the basic unit of natural gas consumption that measures the quantity of gas energy flowing through the pipes. One therm is equal to 100,000 btu.

The Horsepower of an Electrical Motor

The horse power of a 230 volts electrical motor with 85 percent efficiency pulling 10 amps can be calculated as:

$P_{hp} = 0.85 (230 \text{ V}) (10 \text{ amps}) / 746 = 2.62 \text{ hp}$

At 85 percent efficiency a one hp motor would use 877 watts per hour.

UNTANGLING YOUR UTILITY BILLS

The electric industry separates the cost of electricity into the following parts:

- Production (generation)
- Transmission (bulk movement of power)
- Distribution (local deliver, metering and billing services
- Transmission and Distribution are often referred to as "Delivery. "

Gas service separates costs for gas as follows:

- Production (the natural gas commodity)
- Transmission (bulk movement of gas from one region to another via interstate pipelines)
- Distribution (the local delivery, metering and billing).

The delivery related costs for electricity will be approximately 5 cents per kWh. In California, this includes about one half cent per kWh to cover California Department of Water Resources (DWR) bond charges incurred to pay for the electricity bought by that agency, during the manipulated energy crisis caused by Enron and other utility companies.

In the California desert, the local utility companies now have a summer base-line allocation of 47.6 kWh per day. The winter base-line allocation is 9.8 kWh per day. Usage over this baseline becomes more expensive. For example, the allocation and prices for the 2,800 square foot house were approximately as follows:

In 2006, the maximum summer baseline allocation was 1,476 kWh (31 days). This costs about 12 cents per kWh or $177.00.

Prices rise steeply depending on how much usage is over the base-line allocation. In 2006 the costs were as follows:

Over Baseline: 1 to 30 percent cost 0.19 cents per kWh
Over Baseline: 31 to 100 percent cost 0.26 cents per kWh
Over Baseline: 100 percent cost 0.37 cents per kWh

In other words, the over Baseline summer usage of 741 kWh costs about $274.00, or three times as much per kWh as the base line allotment.

To give you an idea of the effect global warming is having on energy usage: During July 2006 in the California desert, the hottest summer on record with some days exceeding 120 degrees, the electric usage on the 2800 square foot house was 4,116 kWh. Two years ago the usage on the same house was 2,598 kWh.

You can see why it makes sense to reduce your energy consumption.

CHECK THE EFFICIENCY OF YOUR AIR CONDITIONER

From the above figures, you can see that the major portion of the electric bill is used in cooling the home. Therefore, it makes sense to check on the efficiency of your air conditioning unit.

A lot of older furnace air handlers and duct systems are not delivering anywhere near the air conditioner's btuh and SEER ratings. Why not? Some problems may include:

- Inadequate cubic feet per minute of a balanced air flow through the evaporator coil circuits.
- Dirty fins/coils and lint filled blower wheel blades.
- Improper location of supply diffusers and return air grills, which can result in inefficient floor level recirculation of the cold conditioned air and lack of a proper heat load through the evaporator coil.

Before you begin working on your air-conditioner, make sure the power to the unit is turned off. If you pick a warm day for the maintenance, you'll get a better idea of why your air conditioner is not working well.

An easy item to fix is cleaning the fins in the compressor unit outside and the evaporator coils inside on the air handler. Follow these simple steps:

1. Remove the grill cover from the condenser carefully (do not pull any wires loose) and clean the fins by using a soft cloth and brush. Fins can be damaged easily, so be careful.
2. Vacuum.
3. After cleaning, hose out the fins after you protect the motor with some kind of waterproof covering.

These items are straightforward and should not present any problems. However, if you run into difficulty, contact the manufacturer for information.

MEASURING AIR CONDITIONER PERFORMANCE

Because there are so many different terms, many homeowners are confused about air conditioner capacity and duct efficiency. However, there are basically two kinds of measures of air conditioner performance:

Tonnage

Tonnage describes how much cooling an air conditioner provides. One ton of air conditioning equals 12,000 btuh.

However, tonnage can be misleading since a 3-ton air conditioner may perform like a 2-ton or even a 1-ton air conditioner because of problems such as low air handler flow or inadequate refrigerant charge. Or perhaps much of the cooling is lost through duct leakage or conduction losses, which combined can diminish the useful cooling capacity of an air conditioner.

SEER RATING

The second measurement used for air conditioners is Seasonal Energy Efficiency Ratio (SEER). The standard for newly installed air conditioners has changed from SEER 10 to SEER 13: a 30 percent increase in efficiency.

For those with older homes built before 1992, switching to an air conditioner with a SEER 13 can provide substantial savings. Many of these older homes were built with units with SEER ratings of only 6 or 7 and the nameplate capacity may have been an overstatement. By doubling the efficiency, reduction in electricity costs and payback in savings will be felt immediately.

The price difference between a SEER 10 and a SEER 13 in a two-and-a-half ton unit, including the cost of a matching evaporator coil if needed per price quotes is about $600.

Additional costs may include sheet-metal work around the new, larger evaporator coil at the furnace and possibly new copper tubing from the compressor to the evaporator. Current plumbing may also need to be cleaned or replaced. In addition, the new units require 40 percent more freon.

Despite speculation that the new outside units will be much larger, according to manufacturers such as Amana, Goodman and Bryant, new units will be the same size or smaller than the current SEER 10 units.

A new digital thermostat is recommended for more efficient operation if your unit has an older analog thermostat. In 2010, the current R-22 air conditioner coolant will be changed to R-410A. At least one manufacturer, Carrier, already includes this new coolant with new air conditioners.

HEAT PUMP RATINGS

The efficiency of a heat pump is indicated by two ratings: one for heating and one for cooling.

The heating rating is called the Heating Seasonal Performance Factor (HSPF); the cooling rating is the same as air conditioners, Seasonal Energy Efficiency Ratio (SEER). In both cases, the higher the number, the greater the efficiency and the lower the operating cost.

If you decide to replace the unit, keep in mind the following suggestions:

1.   Check credentials.
2.   The dealer should be affiliated with a nationally known manufacturer.
3.   Ask for references.
4.   Expect an on-site evaluation visit.

5. Check local licenses.

6. Don't be afraid to ask questions.

7. Get a cost estimate.

8. Inquire about equipment and labor warranties.

9. Ask about preventative maintenance programs.

10. Insist on a written proposal.

BENEFITS OF AN ENERGY CALCULATION

Because some in-place air conditioner compressor units are over-sized, request a Manual J Energy Calculation. Some air conditioning firms tend to over-size the units to increase profits and you may be able to downsize.

A properly sized air conditioner based on the needs of your house is important. For example, a 5-ton, 6 SEER rated unit could possibly be replaced with a 3-ton 13 SEER rated unit, resulting in reduced replacement costs and a more efficient operation. A smaller unit can reduce humidity and repair bills since oversized units tend to cycle on and off repeatedly.

The following is the electrical usage for various sized 10 SEER compressor units based on manufacturer's data:

2 ton	11.2 amps	2.576 kWh
2.5 ton	13.6 amps	3.128 kWh
3 ton	16.9 amps	3.887 kWh

| 4 ton | 22.3 amps | 4.419 kWh |
| 5 ton | 28.1 amps | 6.463 kWh |

At the base rate of 12 cents per kWh, it costs 77 cents an hour to run a 5-ton air, 10 SEER, conditioning unit.

However, if you go over the baseline usage by 100 percent where I live in the California desert, it currently costs about $2.39 an hour to cool your home with a 10 SEER 5-ton air conditioner.

Electric costs in the California desert are extreme. I know a retired doctor who owns a house that is not energy efficient and zoned with two 5-ton units and one 3-ton unit. He paid $2100 for an electric bill in July 2006. If he goes 100 percent over the baseline rate, it costs $6 per hour to run his air conditioners.

Replacing the compressor with a 13 SEER can reduce costs by 30 percent. If you replace an old 5-ton unit with a 4-ton compressor, you can save even more money.

In addition, less usage means less carbon to the atmosphere and you'll be doing your part to cut down on global warming.

You can download a simple energy calculating program on the Internet at www.energycodes.gov. The program is called *Rescheck.*

Using this program, you can compute the energy needs of your house and see how it compares with the minimum requirements of the code. Experiment with the program and see how much energy efficiency improves if you add slab edge insulation. In the sample 1320 square foot steel framed house detailed later in this book, the savings was 7 percent, a considerable savings for little investment.

The program also includes a user-friendly manual you can download as well as a package generator for energy calculations. In addition, this site provides plenty of excellent information on how to make your home more energy efficient.

DUCT EFFICIENCY

Duct efficiency measures how much of the cooling is lost through duct leakage and conduction losses.

If duct efficiency is only 75 percent, it reduces the cooling of a 4-ton unit to the equivalent of three tons of air conditioning.

Have your ducts tested for leakage and add insulation to your ducts if they are located in the attic.

SWIMMING POOLS

Pool Pumps

Check how many hours your pool pump is running. A two horsepower motor at 85 percent efficiency uses 1754 kWh. At 37 cents per kWh, it costs 65 cents per hour to run the pump. If you run the pump eight hours each day, your monthly cost will be $156 per month. Experiment to find out the minimum time needed to keep the pool clean and save money.

Pool Covers

If you don't use the pool daily, consider covering it when not in use. Aside from safety issues, investing in a pool cover can save you money. How?

- If you are heating your pool, a pool cover helps retain heat lost to the atmosphere by evaporation.

- A pool cover helps keep the water clean and you'll need fewer chemicals.

- You can run your pump a shorter period of time, especially if you are using a salt water system.

Chapter Eight

BUILDING AN ENVIRONMENTALLY AND ENERGY EFFICIENT STEEL FRAMED HOUSE

In 1999, the Coachella Valley Housing Coalition (a non-profit organization located in Indio, California) asked me to provide designs for energy efficient housing that could be built by untrained homeowners. The homeowners provided "sweat equity" as a down payment.

In the past seven years, hundreds of these homes have been built and proven to be energy efficient. In 2000, we received the highest award (platinum) at the National Association of Homebuilders Convention in Atlanta from the United States Housing and Urban Development (HUD).

Below is a portion of a letter received earlier from the Secretary of HUD announcing my selection for the "Building Innovation for Home Ownership Award" dated October 16, 1996. The award was for the design of a simple, energy efficient, and affordable steel framed house similar to the one detailed in this book.

I applaud you for your efforts. Your project is a fine example of how the best of American creativity and innovation can help expand homeownership opportunities for all Americans.

Sincerely,

Henry Cisneros

Henry G. Cisneros

Habitat for Humanity utilized the simple, energy efficient plan using an all woman volunteer crew and constructed the house in only seven days.

In 1998, McGraw Hill published a book I co-authored, *Residential Steel Design and Construction: Energy Efficiency, Cost Saving and Code Compliance.* The book, now out of print, outlined how to construct simple energy efficient steel framed houses and was directed toward architects, engineers and building contractors. That same year, I received a letter from an Engineer in the Dominican Republic who had followed the details in the book and built a house that survived Hurricane George in an area where other houses were destroyed. Although the house was not designed specifically to withstand hurricanes forces, building codes for steel construction requires a 100 percent safety factor that makes these homes resistant to hurricanes as well as earthquakes.

Illustrations and drawings in this book are meant to be a guide. You should obtain the services of a professional engineer in your area to provide construction plans and incorporate any requirements that local building officials may have. Wind and snow loads vary in different parts of the country.

This book is written to show how you can construct a house that is energy efficient. Keep in mind; however, your lifestyle determines how much energy savings you'll achieve.

If you make the decision to build a steel frame house, take comfort in the fact that over a thousand houses have been built here in the Coachella Valley by untrained workers. If you follow the guidelines in this book, you should be successful framing and sheathing your own house.

MODEL HOUSE CONSTRUCTED BY STUDENTS

The basic floor plan for this house can be modified to be constructed as a three or four bedroom model, and turned sideways to fit on narrow lots. The above picture is a finished home constructed by students with Building Horizons.

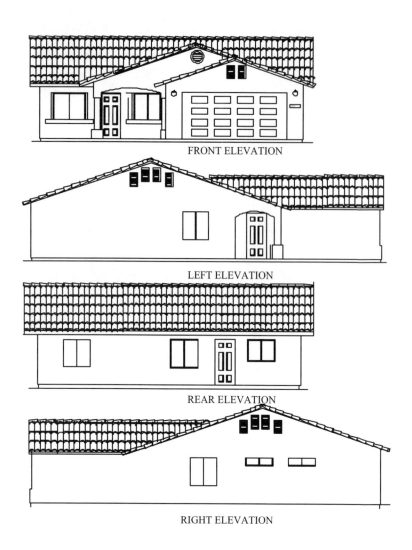

FRONT ELEVATION

LEFT ELEVATION

REAR ELEVATION

RIGHT ELEVATION

ELEVATIONS FOR THE FOUR BEDROOM MODEL

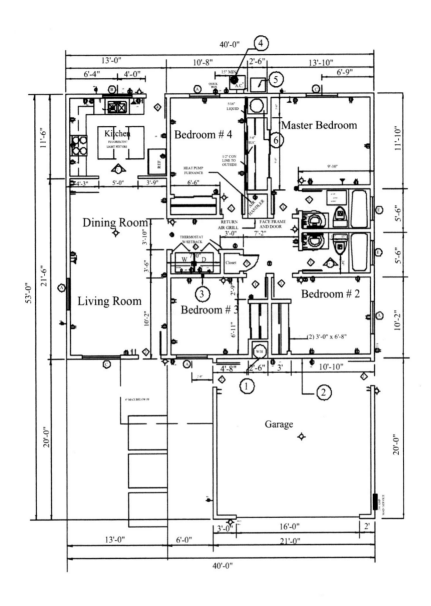

FOUR BEDROOM FLOOR PLAN

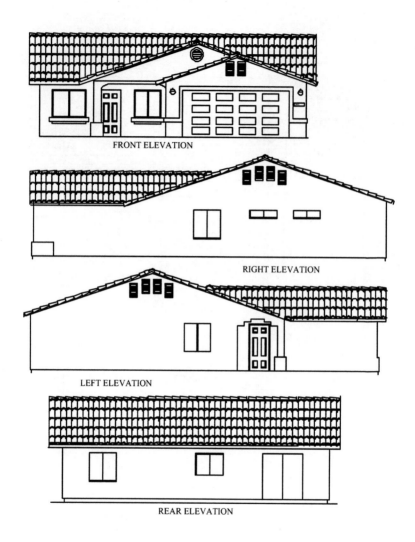

FRONT ELEVATION

RIGHT ELEVATION

LEFT ELEVATION

REAR ELEVATION

THREE BEDROOM ELEVATIONS

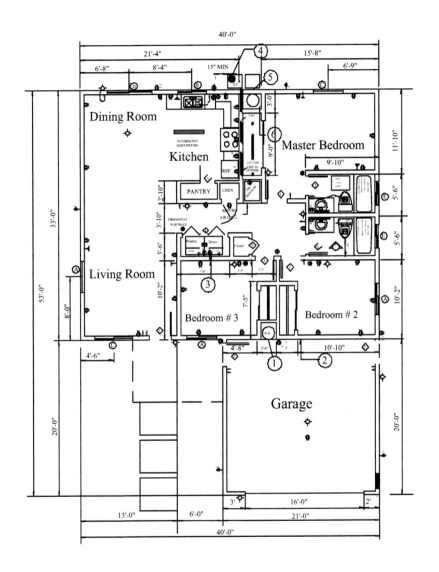

THREE BEDROOM FLOOR PLAN

61

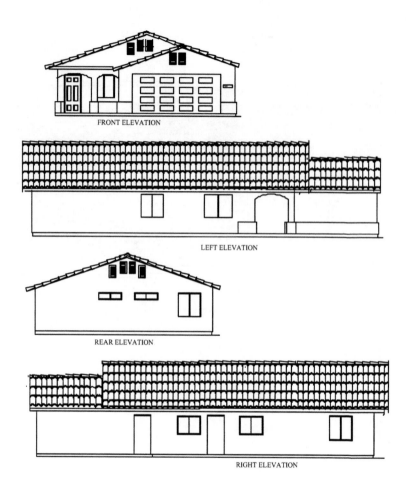

FRONT ELEVATION

LEFT ELEVATION

REAR ELEVATION

RIGHT ELEVATION

SLIM MODEL ELEVATIONS

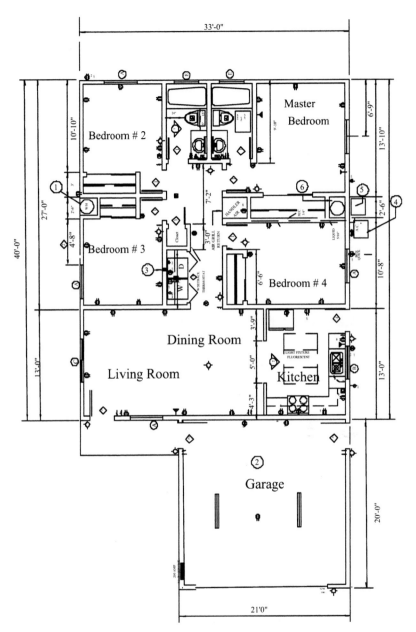

SLIM MODEL FOUR BEDROOM FLOOR PLAN

GENERAL NOTES FOR ALL FLOOR PLANS:

1. Install a high efficiency gas water heater with auto pilot ignition and pressure relief valve on an 18-inch high platform for the water heater. Provide 5/8-inch type "X" gypsum board on top of the platform and all sides. Install earthquake straps (2) ¾-inch by 24 gauge straps with ¼-inch bolts attached direct to framing.

2. Install 5/8-inch type "X" gypsum wallboard from floor to ceiling between garage and living space.

3. Install 4-inch metal dryer vent to exterior with maximum of two 90 degree bends with a damper. Install louver doors on the laundry room or install an exhaust fan with a damper to outside air.

4. Install a high efficiency 13 SEER air conditioner compressor on a concrete pad 3 inches above grade.

5. Install a 4000 cubic foot per minute evaporative cooler on a concrete pad 3 inch above grade.

6. Install a 24-inch square duct chase. Lower the closet ceiling to 7 feet as needed to provide access to the attic. The outlet registers should have back draft dampers. Install "UpDux" outlets into the attic that close when not in use.

Provide garage ventilation 12 x 12 inch screen vents up 12 inches from floor and 12 inches down from ceiling.

Provide a 4' x 4' minimum concrete landing at each exterior door a maximum of 4 inches below the finish floor of the house.

Provide a 22 x 33 inch attic access.

WINDOWS

Windows should be vinyl framed dual pane, argon gas filled with a minimum U-value of 0.40.

A) Denotes 4'-0"x4' -0" horizontal sliding windows
B) Denotes 4'-0"x 3'-0" horizontal sliding windows
C) Denotes 4'-0"x 5'-0" single hung vertical windows
D) Denotes 5'-0"x 6'-8" horizontal sliding doors
E) Denotes 4'-0"x 1'-0" horizontal sliding windows

DOORS

Doors should be as listed:

1. Denotes 2'-6"x 6'-8" hollow interior door
2. Denotes 3'-0"x 6'-8" metal with R-6 insulation
3. Denotes 2'-0"x 6'-8" hollow interior door
4. Denotes 2'-6"x 6'-8" louvered (laundry area)

If solid doors are installed in the laundry area, a power vent is required for the area.

ELECTRICAL NOTES

Electrical system bonding shall comply with NEC 250-81, to wit: Each system noted below shall be bonded together to form the grounding electrode system. The bonding jumper shall be sized in accordance with Section 250-79(c) and shall be connected in direct contact with the earth for 10 feet or more and electrically continuous to the points of connection of the grounding electrode conductor and the bonding conductors. Continuity of the grounding path or the bonding connection to interior piping shall not rely on water meters. A metal underground water pipe shall be supplemented by an additional electrode of a type specified in section 250-81 or in section 250-83.2. An electrode encased by at least 2 inches of concrete, located within and near the bottom of concrete foundation or footing that is in direct contact with earth, consisting of at least 20 feet of one or more steel reinforcing bars or rods of not less than ½ inch diameter, or consisting of at least 20 feet of bars copper conductor no smaller than No. 2 AWG.

Main service panel shall be grounded per NEC 250-83, to wit: 1 #2/0 in 1 inch conduit to accessible cold water main, bonded per NEC 250-83, table 250-94. Grounding system includes continuous bond from panel to ufer ground, cold water piping and gas piping system.

All smoke detectors shall be 110V and wired to building electrical system, with battery back-up; all detectors shall be wired together to sound a common alarm to any fire.

All convenience outlets outside of residential structures or with laundry, bathrooms and garages shall be ground-fault interruption circuit protected.

All electrical outlets in all bedrooms, including lighting, smoke detectors, outlets, are to have arc-fault interrupters protection. NEC Sec. 210.12(B)

Light switches in the kitchen and bath to be manual on, motion off, with 4 pin 24-watt florescent fixtures. Use energy-saving ballasts on all fluorescent lighting.

Garage light to be on a photo cell with florescent 12 watt bulb and an illuminated building numbers address 4-inch high numbers connected to photo cell.

Fixtures in shower and tub areas shall be listed for damp locations, per NEC 410-04.

Openings around electrical penetrations through fire-resistive rated walls, partitions, floors or ceilings shall be fire-stopped using approved methods to maintain the fire-resistive rating.

MECHANICAL NOTES

All mechanical work and material shall be in full accordance to the "Uniform Mechanical Code" latest edition. This includes all state, county, fire, health department and local codes. All mechanical units to bear appropriate labels as specified.

All round ducts shall be low pressure flexible duct, as manufactured by "Casco Co. Type SL-181" or equal. All joints shall be securely fastened together with screws and approved duct tape, with adequate metal supports. The insulation shall be a minimum of R-8.

All rectangular ducts shall be new galvanized iron, fabricated and installed as per "SMACNA" recommendations. Provide 1½-inch duct liner with .16 thermal conductance for all exposed duct work. Provide 2-inch R-8.0 insulation blanket type for all interior duct work. Provide and install approved fire dampers as per local and state codes as required.

Provide smooth metal duct for dryer exhaust. Dryer ducts shall not exceed a total combined horizontal and vertical length of 14 feet including two 90 degree elbows. Two feet shall be deducted for each 90 degree elbow in excess of two. The dryer duct shall have a back draft damper per UMC 1901.

All air ducts penetrating separation wall or ceiling between garage and living area shall be 26 gauge minimum.

Plumber to provide all gas and condensate facilities including final connections to the equipment specified.

Electrician to provide all electrical facilities as required including thermostats, by-pass timer box, and all conduit to units and components with final connections.

General Contractor to provide all openings, curbs, equipment platforms, and adequate structural support for the air conditioners and related equipment as specified.

Bathroom fans shall provide 5 air changes per hour.

PLUMBING NOTES

Provide pressure regulator for any water service which exceeds 80 PSI.

Provide non-removable back flow prevention devices on all exterior hose bibs.

A minimum access panel to bathtub trap connection is required. All toilets to be "ULTRA LOW FLUSH." All interior faucets shall have a maximum 2.2 gallons per minute (GPM) flow. All shower heads shall have a max 2-5 GPM flow.

ATTIC VENTILATION

Note: 1320 square feet building of attic area divided by 150 equals 8.8 square feet of ventilation required. 8.8 square feet x 144 = 1287 square inches. A 15" x 24" gable vent has approximately 200 square inches of net open area. 1287 divided by 200 requires a minimum of 7 vents for the main house.

The garage of 420 square feet divided by 150 equals 2.8 square feet x 144 = 403 square feet or 2 vents.

ROOF

Provide minimum No. 28 gauge galvanized iron valley flashing and No. 26 gauge galvanized iron flashing and counter flashing at junction of roof and vertical surfaces.

BUILDING CODES

UBC:1997 Edition, UPC: 2000 Edition, UMC: 2000 Edition, NEC: 1999 Edition. Cabo: one and two family dwelling code, 1996/1997 amended. Occupancy Group single family R-3/U-1. Type of construction V-N.

CHAPTER NINE
FOUNDATION DETAILS

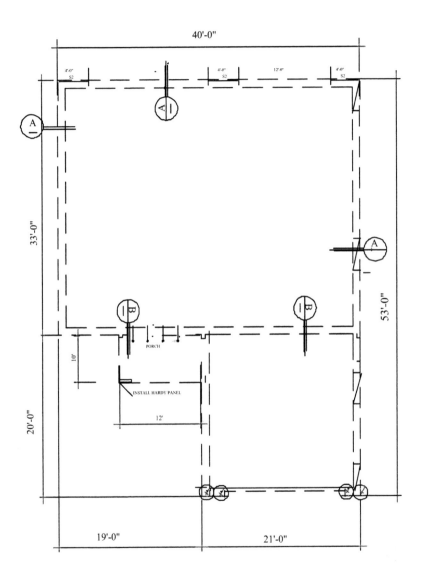

TYPICAL FOUNDATION BOTH MODELS

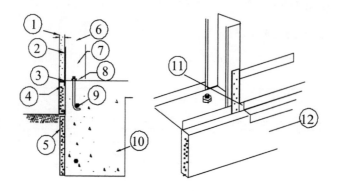

SECTION "A" INSULATED FOUNDATION

1. One coat stucco system with 1" foam insulation per ICC-ESR 1194 or equal.
2. Attach hold down strap with (14) #10 screws.
3. Install 1½" x 1½" 26 gauge "Z" flashing and"J" metal weep screed.
4. Install 6"x 1½" or 1" extruded foam insulation attach and coat with poly bond.
5. Install 12" x 1½" or 1" extruded foam insulation. Install prior to pouring concrete footing.
6. 3½, 4" studs at 24" o.c. 20 gauge galvanized.
7. Minimum R-13 wall insulation.
8. 20 gauge bottom track, caulked to foundation.
9. Anchor bolt where specified or Simpson MAS mud sill anchor as an alternate.
10. Concrete foundation 12" x 18" with (2) #4 rebars.
11. Screw Z-metal to track over foam insulation.
12. Coat exposed face with elastomeric copolymer brush able sealant and paint to match exterior finish.

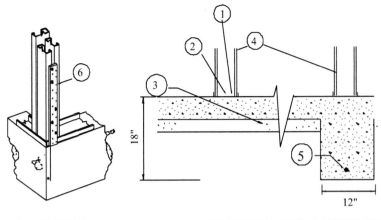

SIMPSON
HOLDDOWN

SECTION "B" INTERIOR
NON-BEARING AND
BEARING WALLS.

1. Install 3/8" shot pins @ 36" o.c. Ramset #3348 or equal, on non-bearing walls only. No foundation is required. Install 5/8" anchor bolts where the wall is a bearing or shear wall.
2. 25 gauge metal track, caulk to foundation and screw to stud with #10 x ½" screws.
3. It is recommended that the slab be installed with 6 x 6 x 10 x 10 welded wire mesh or #3 rebar at 18" o.c. over 2" compacted sand over 10 mill visqueen or per soils report specifications.
4. 25 gauge metal studs at 24" o.c. Use 3½" 20 gauge at shear panels and 4" 20 gauge at all other locations for bearing walls.
5. Install #4 rebars top and bottom of foundation.
6. Simpson HPAHD22. Install per manufacturers specifications.

RAISED FLOOR FRAMING DETAILS USING STEEL JOISTS

Many contractors find that framing a raised floor with steel joists more time consuming and expensive than framing the floor with wood joists. This does not have to be the case. This section discusses the basic differences in framing a raised foundation with wood and simple time-saving details you can use when framing with steel.

Duplicating a typical steel-framed raised floor using the same details as wood construction will create problems.

A 2-inch wood joist or rim joist supports vertical loads perpendicular to its side very well. However, the web on a steel stud will bend when subjected to the wall load. This is called web crippling. Depending on the vertical load, you may have to install two rim joists plus web stiffeners at the joints. In addition, the floor joists must be aligned with the wall stud.

Keep in mind that while a steel stud has little strength due to web crippling, it has a great deal of strength when subjected to shear. In addition, screw connections are strong. To utilize this strength, consider an alternate design for raised floors when using steel.

Figure 2 below has been used successfully on various projects and proven easy to construct. It eliminates the need for rim joists and angle clips to tie the floor to the foundation. This not only saves time, but best of all, saves money on materials.

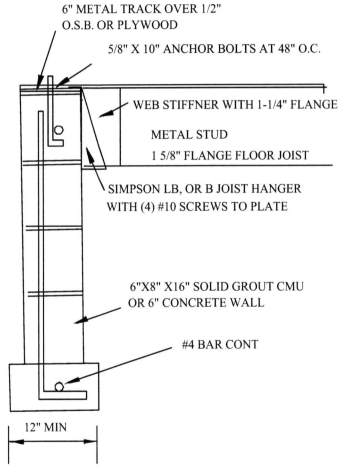

6" METAL TRACK OVER 1/2"
O.S.B. OR PLYWOOD

5/8" X 10" ANCHOR BOLTS AT 48" O.C.

WEB STIFFNER WITH 1-1/4" FLANGE

METAL STUD

1 5/8" FLANGE FLOOR JOIST

SIMPSON LB, OR B JOIST HANGER
WITH (4) #10 SCREWS TO PLATE

6"X8" X16" SOLID GROUT CMU
OR 6" CONCRETE WALL

#4 BAR CONT

12" MIN

FIG.2-RAISED FLOOR USING STEEL JOISTS

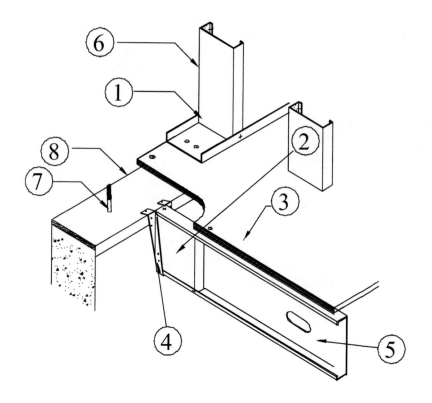

FLOOR JOISTS PERPENDICULAR
TO EXTERIOR WALL

1. 4" x1 ¼" track attach with two screws to each stud.
2. Bearing stiffener stud 1 ¼" flange to fit between floor joist flanges web facing out.
3. ¾" T & G sheathing.
4. Simpson LB, or B joist hanger with (4) #10 screws to plate.
5. Metal stud floor joist.
6. Wall stud.
7. 5/8" anchor bolt at 48" o.c.
8. 6" metal track over ½" OSB or plywood strip.

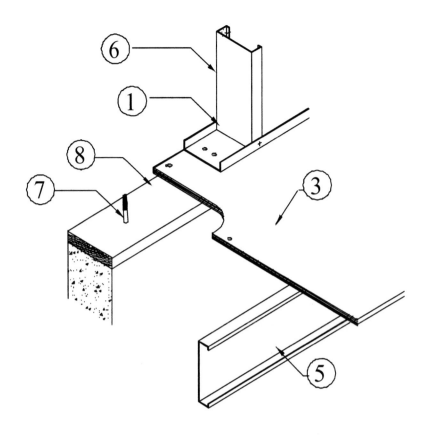

FLOOR JOISTS PARALLEL
TO EXTERIOR WALL

To use these details, set the top of the block or concrete foundation at an elevation 1 ¼ inches below the finished floor elevation. Install anchor bolts as required by code. Install a strip of ½-inch foundation grade plywood or OSB through the anchor bolts; install a metal track over the strip and attach joist hangers. Install a 1 ¼-inch flange web stiffener at the end of the floor joists and screw to the joist hanger. Unlike wood construction, the contact of steel to concrete is not a problem.

Install the bottom plate on a raised foundation by snapping out the interior wall lines using a chalk line. Use a 4″ x 4″ section of wood to align the track with the anchor bolts. Install the bottom plate by using a ¾-inch iron pipe and a hammer to punch through the anchor bolt.

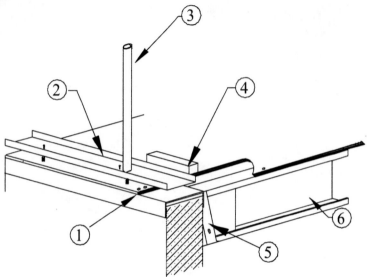

INSTALLATION OF BOTTOM TRACK

1. Install bead of caulking to top of sub floor material prior to installing bottom track. Screw flooring to track with No. 8 @ 12″ o.c.
2. 4″ x 1 ¼″ minimum 20 gauge track.
3. Use ¾″ iron pipe and a hammer to punch through the anchor bolt.
4. Use 4″ x 4″ stud as guide to install track parallel with chalk line.
5. Simpson LB or B joist hangers.
6. Floor joist with bearing stiffeners.

With this method of construction, you don't need to align the floor joists under the wall studs. You can space the joists at 16-inch o.c. even if the wall studs are at 24-inch o.c.

At 24-inch o.c., a ¾-inch OSB or plywood sub-floor causes the top flange of the stud to flex, unlike a wood stud, which causes vibration. Spacing the floor joists at 16-inch o.c. will solve this problem. Some experts suggest using a higher gauge stud for the floor joist; however, this causes an increase in thermal bridging and raises the cost of materials.

Using Table 506.3.2 of the Cabo code for steel joists at 24-inch o.c., a 9' 7" span at 40 PSF live load, requires a 2 x 6 x 54 (16 gauge). However, at 16-inch o.c., you can use a 2 x 6 x 33 (20 gauge). The 16-inch o.c. span helps eliminate vibration and costs about the same for joists as the 54 at 24-inch o.c.

In addition, it is easier to screw plywood to 33 (20 gauge) than to 54 (16 gauge). If you install steel floor joists at 24-inch o.c., consider adding a second layer of ½-inch plywood or OSB over the ¾-inch sub-floor to eliminate vibration. I found out the hard way, a single layer of ¾-inch is not acceptable on 24-inch o.c.. In fact, I've found it necessary to go back on projects and add the extra layer to stairs and floors.

GENERAL NOTES

1. Concrete shall be 2500 psi @ 28 days or as required by a soils report. All exterior walls shall have ½" anchor bolts at 24" o.c. (5/8" in seismic zone 4). Bolts shall have 3-inch square washers.

2. All interior non-bearing walls shall have 3/8" shot pins @ 48" o.c. ramset No. 3348 or equal, unless otherwise noted.

3. All footings shall have (2) #4 rebars, 1-top, 1-bottom, typical.

4. The concrete slab shall be minimum 4 inches thick with reinforcing: welded wire mesh, 10 x 10 x 6 x 6 or #3 rebar at 18" o.c. mid depth, or as required by a soils report. Install over 10 mil visqueen and compacted 3" sand fill.

5. The foundation slab shall be insulated per section "A" detail on page 72.

6. Care shall be taken to install the forms for the building slab level, and square. 6-inch steel studs can be used as forms in place of wood and will give a straighter edge. This is important since the wall studs can only be adjusted ½-inch up and down to compensate for valleys in the concrete.

CHAPTER TEN
FRAMING DETAILS

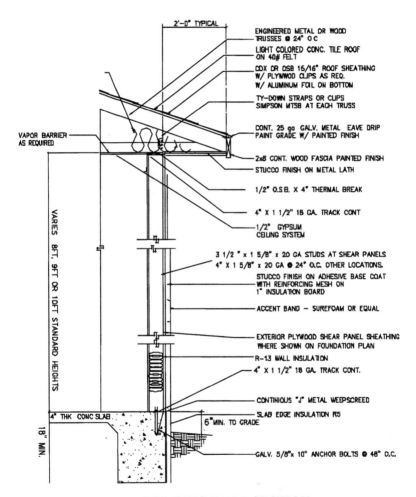

2'-0" TYPICAL

ENGINEERED METAL OR WOOD
TRUSSES @ 24" O C

LIGHT COLORED CONC. TILE ROOF
ON 40# FELT

CDX OR OSB 15/16" ROOF SHEATHING
W/ PLYWOOD CLIPS AS REQ.
W/ ALUMINUM FOIL ON BOTTOM

TY-DOWN STRAPS OR CLIPS
SIMPSON MTSB AT EACH TRUSS

CONT. 25 ga GALV. METAL EAVE DRIP
PAINT GRADE W/ PAINTED FINISH

VAPOR BARRIER
AS REQUIRED

2x8 CONT. WOOD FASCIA PAINTED FINISH
STUCCO FINISH ON METAL LATH

1/2" O.S.B. X 4" THERMAL BREAK

4" X 1 1/2" 18 GA. TRACK CONT

1/2" GYPSUM
CEILING SYSTEM

3 1/2 " x 1 5/8" x 20 GA STUDS AT SHEAR PANELS
4" X 1 5/8" x 20 GA @ 24" O.C. OTHER LOCATIONS.

STUCCO FINISH ON ADHESIVE BASE COAT
WITH REINFORCING MESH ON
1" INSULATION BOARD

ACCENT BAND — SUREFOAM OR EQUAL

EXTERIOR PLYWOOD SHEAR PANEL SHEATHING
WHERE SHOWN ON FOUNDATION PLAN

R-13 WALL INSULATION

4" X 1 1/2" 18 GA. TRACK CONT.

CONTINIOUS "J" METAL WEEPSCREED

SLAB EDGE INSULATION R5

6" MIN. TO GRADE

GALV. 5/8"x 10" ANCHOR BOLTS @ 48" O.C.

VARIES 8FT, 9FT OR 10FT STANDARD HEIGHTS

4" THK CONC SLAB

18" MIN.

TYPICAL BUILDING WALL SECTION

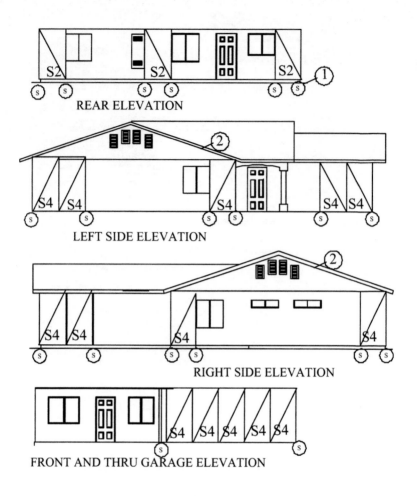

REAR ELEVATION

LEFT SIDE ELEVATION

RIGHT SIDE ELEVATION

FRONT AND THRU GARAGE ELEVATION

SHEAR WALL LOCATIONS FOR 4 BEDROOM HOUSE

1. (19) S/HPAHD22 required. Install one at each corner of each shear wall. Only one is required at the corners.
2. 7/16" OSB with #8 screws at 6 inches over the gable end trusses.

SHEAR WALL SCHEDULE FOR LOCATION OF SCREWS ON EDGE

S2   7/16 OSB   #8x1" @ 4" o.c   Anchor bolts @ 24" o.c.
S4   7/16 OSB   #8x1" @ 2" o.c.   Anchor bolts @ 18" o.c.

Use #8 x 1" @ 12" o.c. in the field typical.

The detail for the four bedroom shear wall can be used with modifications for the three bedroom and the slim model.

The details for the shear wall at the front of the garage are shown on page 88.

NOTES FOR SHEAR WALL INSTALLATION

1. Screws in field of panel shall be installed 12 inches o.c. unless otherwise shown.
2. Minimum three ½" (5/8" in seismic zone 4) anchor bolts per shear wall.
3. Framing screws shall be No. #8 x 5/8" wafer head self-drilling.
4. OSB screws shall be #8 x 1" flat head with a head of 0.292".
5. Drywall screws to be #6 x 1".
6. OSB to be APA rated. Span rated 24/0.
7. Use 3 ½-inch metal studs where shear walls are specified and use 4-inch metal studs at all other locations.

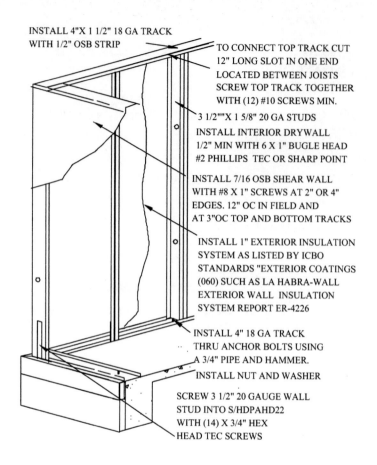

INSTALL 4"X 1 1/2" 18 GA TRACK
WITH 1/2" OSB STRIP

TO CONNECT TOP TRACK CUT
12" LONG SLOT IN ONE END
LOCATED BETWEEN JOISTS
SCREW TOP TRACK TOGETHER
WITH (12) #10 SCREWS MIN.

3 1/2""X 1 5/8" 20 GA STUDS

INSTALL INTERIOR DRYWALL
1/2" MIN WITH 6 X 1" BUGLE HEAD
#2 PHILLIPS TEC OR SHARP POINT

INSTALL 7/16 OSB SHEAR WALL
WITH #8 X 1" SCREWS AT 2" OR 4"
EDGES. 12" OC IN FIELD AND
AT 3"OC TOP AND BOTTOM TRACKS

INSTALL 1" EXTERIOR INSULATION
SYSTEM AS LISTED BY ICBO
STANDARDS "EXTERIOR COATINGS
(060) SUCH AS LA HABRA-WALL
EXTERIOR WALL INSULATION
SYSTEM REPORT ER-4226

INSTALL 4" 18 GA TRACK
THRU ANCHOR BOLTS USING
A 3/4" PIPE AND HAMMER.
INSTALL NUT AND WASHER

SCREW 3 1/2" 20 GAUGE WALL
STUD INTO S/HDPAHD22
WITH (14) X 3/4" HEX
HEAD TEC SCREWS

After the slab is poured, attach the bottom track to the concrete foundation by punching the 4-inch track through the anchor bolts with a ¾-inch iron pipe and a hammer. You can attach the studs to the OSB sheet while flat on the floor. One panel should have the studs on the edges. The adjacent panel should have one stud inside the edge by 4 inches. Install the corners first as shown in the detail and install the top track with a few temporary studs to hold it up. Stretch a line of dental floss from one corner of the shear wall to the other corner of the building. Insert a piece of OSB to raise the dental floss up.

Insert the 4-inch wall studs individually and adjust them in the track to compensate for any unevenness in the slab. Do not frame the wall on the floor and then try to stand it up, you may bend the studs. Use a piece of OSB to set the top track even with the dental floss. This will keep your top plate line level.

When the panels are set into the bottom track and they are screwed together, the building will be plumb and aligned. The doors and windows can be built in a jig as shown on the next drawing. The header is constructed with (2) 6" x 1 5/8" 18 gauge studs for spans less than 5'-4".

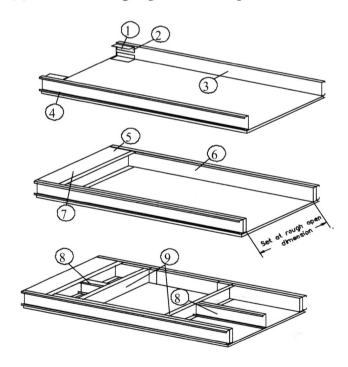

DETAILS FOR WINDOW AND DOOR OPENINGS

CONSTRUCTION NOTES

1. (4) Clip angles 1 ½" x1 ½" (18 gauge) Length = header depth less ½". Set them below top and side of the king stud (item 3) the thickness of the header so it will fit flush with top track.
2. Attach each clip angle to the king stud with (4) #8 screws.
3. King stud.
4. Clamp the king studs at the rough opening dimension to the plywood jig with vise grip clamps, web facing in both sides. (The rough opening for windows is normally the window size; the rough opening for doors is plus 2 inches.)
5. Install rigid insulation in the header stud (attach header to the clip angles (item 1) with (4) #8 screws) each end. Screw backside when you have finished with the front.
6. Install rigid insulation in the king studs.
7. Screw track to header (web facing in) with #8 at 12" o.c.
8. Install metal studs at 24" o.c.
9. Cut flange on track and install at rough height opening dimension. Lap 6" over king studs. Set top track at 6' 8" for windows and 6' 10" for exterior doors.

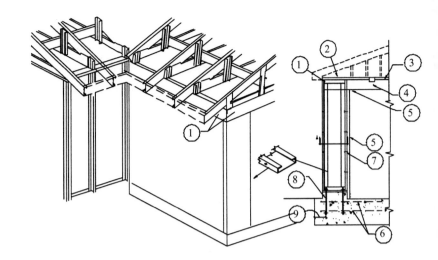

PORCH INSTALLATION DETAILS OF A HARDY PANEL
MODEL 818 WITH 7/8" ANCHOR BOLTS.

1. Notch 6-inch header stud and screw to Hardy Panel with (10) #10 screws.
2. Screw top track to header with #10 screws at 2" o.c.
3. 3 ½" x 1" top track 18 gauge.
4. Porch header (2) 6" x 1 ½" 18 gauge. Connect to bottom chord of truss with 2" x 2" 20-gauge plates at 24" o.c. screw with (4) #8 screws.
5. 3 ½" x 1" 18 gauge track.
6. #4 top and bottom rebars extended 4'-0" past end of each end of frame.
7. 3 ½" x 1 ½" 18 gauge king stud.
8. 7/8" all-thread rod with ½" x 3" x 3" plate washer embed 21".
9. Set all-thread rod 8" from edge of concrete footing.

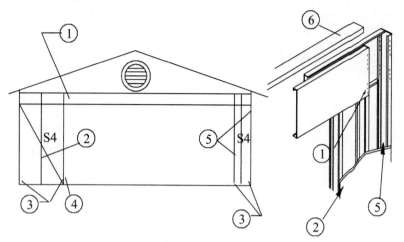

GARAGE HEADER DETAIL

1. (2) 12" x 1 5/8" 16 gauge studs 20' long. Notch at vertical studs and attach to minimum three studs with (10) #10 screws.
2. 7/16" OSB with #8 screws at 2" o.c. both sides. Use 16 gauge studs at each end of shear wall.
3. Simpson S/HPAHD22 with (14) #10 screws each end. And 5/8" anchor bolts at 12" o.c.
4. (2) 3-5/8"x 1 ½" 18 gauge track 16 feet long. Cut flange and bend at connection to header.
5. (3) 18 gauge 3 5/8" studs.
6. 3-5/8" x 1 ½" 18 gauge track 21 feet long as a drag strut. Connect to header stud #8 screws @ 12" o.c.

The garage header can be attached to the studs while flat on the floor. Install the 3 5/8" x 1 ½" 18 gauge tracks around the opening and stand and brace the frame. Install anchor bolts. Install the OSB on both sides screwing it to the plate per the shear detail with #8 screws at 2 o.c. both sides. The hold downs should be screwed over the OSB panel.

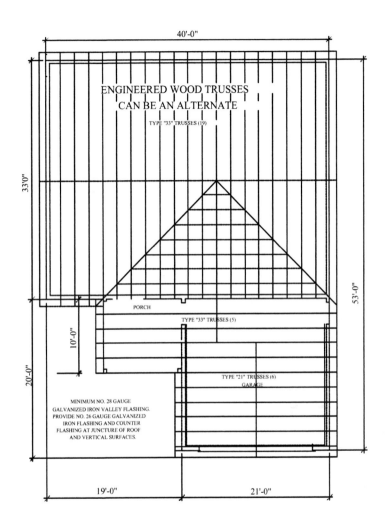

40'-0"

ENGINEERED WOOD TRUSSES
CAN BE AN ALTERNATE

TYPE "33" TRUSSES (19)

33'0"

53'-0"

PORCH

TYPE "33" TRUSSES (5)

10'-0"

TYPE "21" TRUSSES (6)
GARAGE

20'-0"

MINIMUM NO. 28 GAUGE
GALVANIZED IRON VALLEY FLASHING.
PROVIDE NO. 26 GAUGE GALVANIZED
IRON FLASHING AND COUNTER
FLASHING AT JUNCTURE OF ROOF
AND VERTICAL SURFACES.

19'-0"

21'-0"

ROOF FRAMING 3 AND 4 BEDROOM MODELS

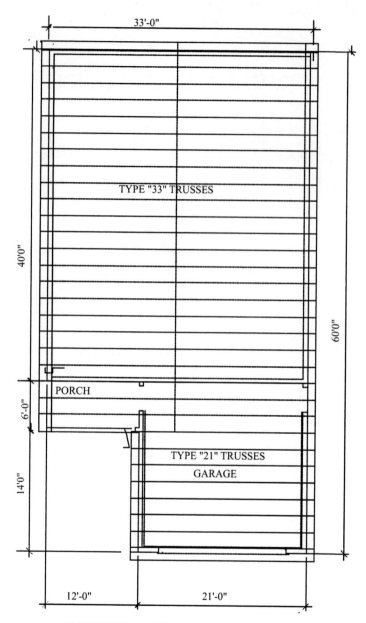

ROOF FRAMING SLIM MODEL

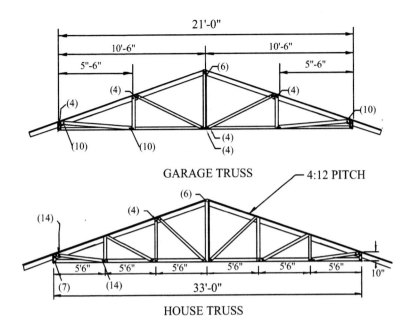

GARAGE TRUSS

HOUSE TRUSS

TYPICAL STEEL TRUSS DETAILS ALL MODELS
(NOT TO SCALE)

The top chord of the garage truss shall be 3 5/8" x 1 5/8" 20 gauge. The top chord of the house truss shall be 6" x 1-5/8" 20 gauge, both un-punched metal studs. Cut flange in middle, angle the cut 2 inches from top to bottom, leave top flange uncut and bend stud. The bottom chord of both trusses and all web members to be 3 5/8" x 1 5/8" 20 gauge un-punched metal studs. All joints to receive (4) #8 hex head screws unless other wise noted above as (14) screws, (10) screws (6) screws, etc.

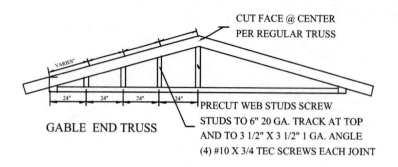

CUT FACE @ CENTER
PER REGULAR TRUSS

VARIES"

24" 24" 24" 24"

GABLE END TRUSS

PRECUT WEB STUDS SCREW
STUDS TO 6" 20 GA. TRACK AT TOP
AND TO 3 1/2" X 3 1/2" 1 GA. ANGLE
(4) #10 X 3/4 TEC SCREWS EACH JOINT

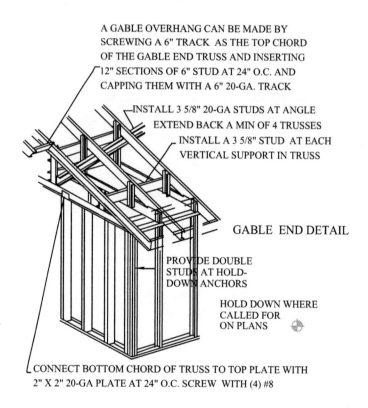

A GABLE OVERHANG CAN BE MADE BY
SCREWING A 6" TRACK AS THE TOP CHORD
OF THE GABLE END TRUSS AND INSERTING
12" SECTIONS OF 6" STUD AT 24" O.C. AND
CAPPING THEM WITH A 6" 20-GA. TRACK

INSTALL 3 5/8" 20-GA STUDS AT ANGLE
EXTEND BACK A MIN OF 4 TRUSSES
INSTALL A 3 5/8" STUD AT EACH
VERTICAL SUPPORT IN TRUSS

GABLE END DETAIL

PROVIDE DOUBLE
STUDS AT HOLD-
DOWN ANCHORS

HOLD DOWN WHERE
CALLED FOR
ON PLANS

CONNECT BOTTOM CHORD OF TRUSS TO TOP PLATE WITH
2" X 2" 20-GA PLATE AT 24" O.C. SCREW WITH (4) #8

GABLE END DETAILS

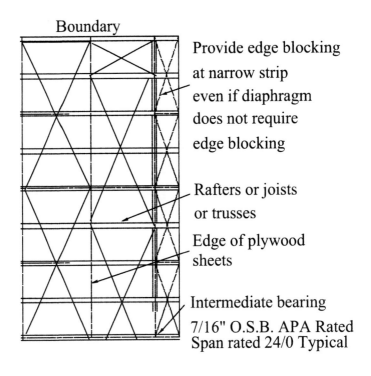

Boundary

Provide edge blocking
at narrow strip
even if diaphragm
does not require
edge blocking

Rafters or joists
or trusses

Edge of plywood
sheets

Intermediate bearing

7/16" O.S.B. APA Rated
Span rated 24/0 Typical

ROOF SHEATHING DETAIL

1. Run long dimension of plywood sheets across (perpendicular to) joists.
2. Stagger plywood end joints 2' 0" minimum on top chord of trusses.
3. Screws shall be as follows with #8 x 1", unless noted otherwise. Boundary: 6 inches o.c. at roof perimeter place lines, chords, struts and as called for on plans. Edge: 6 inches o.c. at bearing ends and edges of each plywood sheet. Field: 12 inches o.c. at all intermediate bearings.
4. All screws shall have a minimum of 3/8" edge distance.

93

5. All joists and rafters shall be laid out in a 4'-0" module to coincide with plywood pattern.

Installing the interior and exterior doors is simple. Install a 20 gauge stud on the hinge side of the pre-hung door. This stud should be plumb. Cut the bottom track at the middle of the door. Cut the flange at the edge of the door and bend it up and screw it to the stud. On the same side as the door knob, set the stud and bend the bottom track like the other side. Set the stud at the rough opening dimension as provided by the manufacturer. Install a 20 gauge track over stud and leave it loose. The header will also have a 20 gauge track. Leave this header track loose.

When you install the pre-hung door, screw the wooden frame into the hinge side. Do not remove the bracing until the other side is screwed into the wood frame. Slide the track over until it fits flush, and screw the wood frame into the 20 gauge track. The door header for the interior walls is installed in a similar manner.

Use a brad nailer to install the wood trim for the door. The brad goes through the gypsum board. When it hits the stud, it bends like a staple.

On exterior walls, the top track should be spliced by cutting a 12 inch long "V" slot in the center of one track and sliding them together. Join using a minimum of (10) #10 screws for the connection.

Chapter Eleven

BUILDING YOUR OWN STEEL TRUSSES

Some builders view the cost and availability of steel trusses as a reason not to use light gauge steel frame designs; however, constructing your own trusses is a fairly simple procedure. There are several reasons to consider this option.

Although several steel manufacturers have developed metal trusses sold in a kit (individual pieces are delivered to the job and assembled in the field) and some wood truss manufacturers are developing steel trusses, these trusses generally cost considerably more than wood and are not yet available in some areas. Sometimes an engineer is hired by the builder to design roof trusses. The builder submits a cut-list to the manufacturer and assembles the trusses at the job site. Unfortunately, these designs can be expensive and complicated.

The steel framing industry has faced an issue common to many new industries and materials: a lack of standardization that limits broad acceptance. However, some common components are beginning to become standards, or at least common practice, for steel frame trusses.

The stress components for trusses found in many engineering handbooks can serve as a basis in designing simple steel trusses. 95

Gussets can be eliminated by attaching webs to chords directly as shown on the sample Howe Truss. Fabricating your own trusses on site can be an easy process if a jig is built and members are precut. Workers with little or no experience can learn how to build steel trusses in a short period of time. For example, women volunteers from a local Home Depot built steel trusses for a Habitat for Humanity project without any problems.

The anatomy and sequence of events of steel frame trusses are basically the same as wood trusses. The basic framing functions also remain the same, although the attachment methods are different. To help you make the transition and understand the purpose of the framing components, we'll take you step-by-step through building a truss.

Before you begin, consider the skill of the framing crew. Builders, constructors, and framers who are not familiar with steel framing construction may require some time, practice and supervision. Ideally, your steel framing crew should consist of one knowledgeable steel framer or lead worker for the layout and cutting and at least two apprentices who can join together the framing components.

Although some builders complain steel trusses are difficult to build, simplifying the design helps. Build a solid jig and lay out the working points carefully. Even a small discrepancy jig can cause hours of heartache in assembly.

Once a jig is built, many builders find two or three workers can assemble a truss in three to five minutes. Don't use camber, steel trusses do not deflect, and lay out the bottom chord flat. The truss illustrated below can be made out of standard metal studs. The design of this truss uses a total load of 40# per square foot. The numbers of screws needed at each connection to construct the truss for the sample house are calculated using the table below. Since loading conditions vary, this design should not be used unless verified by a professional engineer or architect. W=80# x 33'(span)/6=440#, Example at end of member 7-8, (7.5 x440#/250#=14 screws)

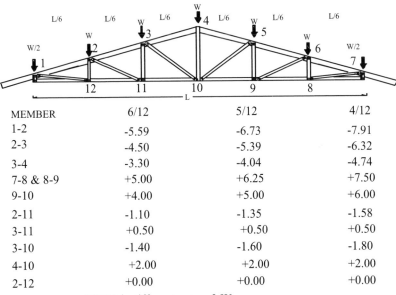

MEMBER	6/12	5/12	4/12
1-2	-5.59	-6.73	-7.91
2-3	-4.50	-5.39	-6.32
3-4	-3.30	-4.04	-4.74
7-8 & 8-9	+5.00	+6.25	+7.50
9-10	+4.00	+5.00	+6.00
2-11	-1.10	-1.35	-1.58
3-11	+0.50	+0.50	+0.50
3-10	-1.40	-1.60	-1.80
4-10	+2.00	+2.00	+2.00
2-12	+0.00	+0.00	+0.00

10" Web stiffner stress = -3 W

+ INDICATES TENSION   - INDICATES COMPRESSON

MAX AXIAL LOAD ON TOP CHORD

6' = 4,000# 7'=2700# 8'=1400#

USE ALLOWABLE LOAD OF 250# FOR EACH #8 TEC SCREW

MAKING A TRUSS WITH A JIG

WOMEN VOLUNTEERS FROM HOME DEPOT MAKING TRUSSES FOR A HABITAT FOR HUMANITY PROJECT.

On the slab, snap out with red chalk lines the truss layout and install 6″ long metal (or wood) stud stops with concrete nails to the slab.

Measure to the center of the top chord of the truss. Bend the top chord of the fill-member by cutting the web and bottom flange at an angle. Do not cut the top flange as this allows the bottom flange to slide inside the adjacent web without having to remove any of the bottom flange. For 6-inch top chords, the cut offset on the bottom flange is half of the roof pitch (2″ for a 4:12 pitch).

Layout the various pre-cut pieces of the truss following the red lines on the slab. Screw them together with hex head screws.

To prevent uplift, provide a tie between the truss and the wall studs by using a commercial connector or installing a strip of strapping with four #8 screws to the 10-inch web stiffener and wall stud. To transfer the roof diaphragm shear to the wall and foundation, the trusses must be blocked. The required strength of truss tie-down connections to resist wind uplift forces can be obtained from Table 802.12 of the CABO code. For example, a house with a 20# design wind load and a 28-foot roof width, including 2-foot overhangs, requires a connection that resists 224#.

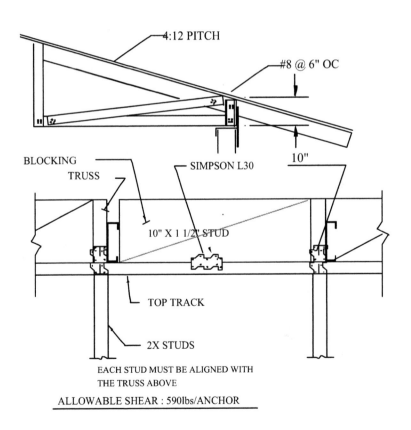

MAKING A "CALIFORNIA FILL" USING THE JIG

Measure from the top of the peak at right angles to the bottom chord a distance equal to two times the roof pitch. Examples for a 6:12 pitch measure 12 inches. Continue marking the jig offsetting this distance down to the top of the top chord at the web stiffener.

Bend the top chord of the fill-member by cutting the web and bottom flange at an angle. (See page 98). Trim the bottom end of the top chord at an angle to fit the roof pitch and assemble the members using a 1 1/2" x 1 1/2" 20 gauge angle as a bottom chord. Install a vertical 3 5/8" x 1 5/8" x 20 gauge stud vertically where the span exceeds 10 feet. Attach to roof plywood with #6 screws at 24" o.c. and the top chord of the building truss.

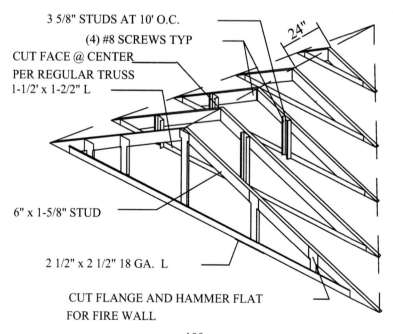

3 5/8" STUDS AT 10' O.C.
(4) #8 SCREWS TYP
CUT FACE @ CENTER
PER REGULAR TRUSS
1-1/2' x 1-2/2" L
24"
6" x 1-5/8" STUD
2 1/2" x 2 1/2" 18 GA. L
CUT FLANGE AND HAMMER FLAT
FOR FIRE WALL

100

Chapter Twelve

INSTALLING INTERIOR WALLS AND GYPSUM BOARD

To prevent convection losses from the interior walls through the ceiling and into the attic, it is recommended that the ceiling have minimum penetrations.

Install ducts within the conditioned space. Soffits can be used to keep the ducts out of the attic or crawl spaces and to add architectural interest. Air conditioning ducts can be installed in a lowered ceiling in the hallway. If you must install ducts in unconditioned spaces, take great care to seal all penetrations of the ceiling and provide connections for the ducts. In the award winning house, supply ducts were installed in the conditioned space below the gypsum board ceiling. A dropped ceiling was used in the hallway, seven feet in height. Ducts should be insulated with R-4 insulation.

Minimize mechanical and electrical runs in insulated wall sections. Eliminate holes in the top track by installing a conduit to a sub-panel located in an interior wall. Install wiring from the sub-panel, running electrical wiring and utility lines in interior walls where possible. If possible, install plumbing within interior walls. Use sconces whenever possible to minimize ceiling fixtures. Give careful attention to caulking and weather stripping. Remember, the overall thermal performance of the completed structure depends on the quality of the construction job.

If possible, the water heater should be located outside the conditioned area as indicated on the floor plan of the award winning house. If at all possible, use a gas-fired water heater even if you need to install a propane tank. Electric resistant water heaters are not energy efficient. However gas-fired water heaters require outside air for combustion. If the water heater compartment is not sealed from the conditioned space, it can be a major source of heat loss or gain and allow infiltration. 5/8" type X gypsum board should be installed inside the water heater compartment on the ceiling, walls, and floor.

After you have installed the trusses, install the gypsum board in the ceiling in one step before you construct any interior walls. The top track of the interior walls can be screwed directly into the drywall of the ceiling without any backing. This will eliminate air from escaping from interior walls into the ceiling and is easier than cutting in each room if you are building your own home.

The interior walls can be framed using 25 gauge material. The bottom plate should be attached to the concrete floor with 3/8" shot pins at 36 inch o.c. The top track is attached directly to the gypsum board ceiling. Backing studs are not needed. In the illustration, some framers install backing studs between the trusses to attach the wall when the ceiling gypsum board is not installed first.

However, extra time and material is required to make this type of connection and you'll have a direct metal to metal connection that transfers heat by conduction from the interior non-insulated walls directly into the steel trusses.

Cracks can also develop at this location and allow convection losses resulting in a design that is not energy efficient.

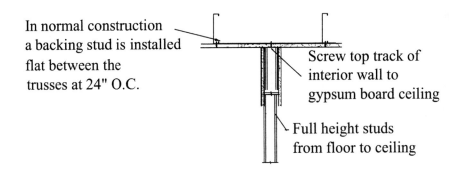

In normal construction a backing stud is installed flat between the trusses at 24" O.C.

Screw top track of interior wall to gypsum board ceiling

Full height studs from floor to ceiling

INTERIOR WALL CONNECTION TO CEILILNG

Backing for the gypsum board at the exterior wall is not necessary, as is typical for wood stud construction. Support the gypsum board ceiling at its edge with a Prest-on clip, as shown below.

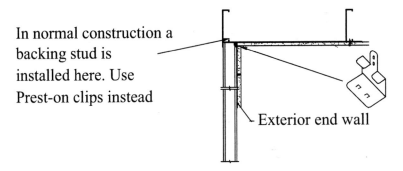

In normal construction a backing stud is installed here. Use Prest-on clips instead

Exterior end wall

CEILING INTERSECTION WITH END WALL

The next item is the wall connection. During wood framing construction, two studs are installed as backing for interior walls. However, using this method in steel stud construction results in a chimney that is difficult to insulate and leaves an open area from the interior walls up to the attic. The two details below show how to leave the interior wall end stud loose. When the gypsum board is installed on the inside of the exterior walls, it can be screwed into the gypsum board. This is called a slammer stud.

Slammer stud. Do not screw to top and bottom track until gypsum board is installed on exterior wall.

In normal construction 3 studs are used at each interior wall connection

screws

INTERIOR WALL CONNECTION TO EXTERIOR WALL

This method eliminates the chimney effect and also stops the convection losses of direct steel to steel contact between the interior walls and the exterior metal stud framing.

When the gypsum wallboard is installed on the exterior walls, use Prest-on corner backing clips at the corners of the exterior walls, as shown in the detail below. This method also eliminates a chimney effect and an area that would be hard to insulate.

In normal construction a stud is installed in this location as backing. Use Prest-on corner back instead.

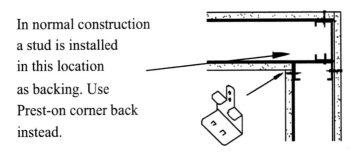

EXTERIOR WALL CORNER CONNECTION

These details have been used in commercial construction for many years, are easy to use and will save you time in framing interior walls. In addition, they eliminate convection losses of direct steel-to-steel contact and reduce the number of metal studs used in the construction. In the model house this amounted to almost 300 lineal feet of 20 gauge studs.

For additional information on steel framing, visit www.toolbase.org.. Select "steel framing," then select "builders' steel stud guide."

Chapter Thirteen

Installing The Interior Finish and Utilities

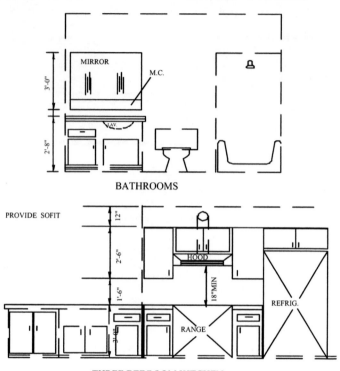

BATHROOMS

THREE BEDROOM KITCHEN

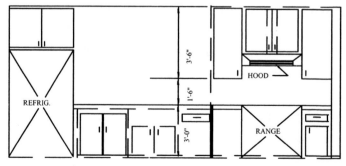

FOUR BEDROOM KITCHEN

ELECTRIC LOAD CALCULATIONS.

```
GEN LIGHTING............. 3 WATTS SQUARE. FT .........................................3960
TWO APPLIANCE CIRCUITS 20 AMPS......................................................3000
LAUNDRY CIRCUIT..................................................................................1500
REFRIGERATOR .........................................................................................700
GARBAGE DISPOSAL...............................................................................1000
FORCED AIR UNIT....................................................................................1200
MICROWAVE............................................................................................1500
YARD LIGHTS...........................................................................................1000
POOL PUMP 2 HP MAX.(OPTIONAL)........................................................2700
SPA PUMP (OPTIONAL).............................................................................2700
TOTAL........................................22,900 VOLT AMPS
FIRST 10 KVA AT100%..........................................................................10.00KVA
12.9 AT 40%...........................................................................................5.16KVA
AC LOAD................................................................................................7.00KVA
ADDITIONAL 100% LOAD.....................................................................10.00KVA
TOTAL 32.16 KVA / 230 VOLTS = 140 AMPS.............................. USE 200 AMP
```

INSTALLING ELECTRIC WIRING

The electric wiring should go from the meter and main to a sub-panel in the house in a conduit under the slab. A separate conduit should be extended to serve the air conditioning unit and evaporative cooler. The wiring from the exterior walls should exit at four feet above the floor level into an interior wall as shown in the illustration on page 109.

Install the smoke alarms on the wall, if possible, instead of the ceiling to avoid additional penetrations through the ceiling. The alarms should be installed high on the wall with the top no closer than 4 inches or further than 12 inches from the ceiling.

In addition, alarms should be no closer than three feet from supply registers of forced air heating systems (which may blow on the alarm preventing it from detecting smoke) and no closer than three feet from the door to a kitchen or a bathroom containing a shower (steam can set the alarm off when the door is opened).

In desert climates, where evaporative coolers are sometimes used, mount smoke alarms on walls 12 inches below the ceiling. These coolers add moisture that can cause the smoke to drop. Since the elderly may have difficulty reaching alarms on the ceiling to change the batteries, mounting the alarms 12 inches lower on the wall is a benefit for them.

USING SCONCES OR WALL MOUNTED LIGHTS

Wall sconces can offer creative options and make an aesthetic statement. The main benefit of a wall sconce is that it eliminates another opening through the ceiling. Each penetration of the ceiling is a potential location for convection losses. These penetrations should be kept to a minimum.

Wall sconces are generally installed at a height of 66 to 72 inches above floor level (rooms with vaulted ceilings can take a higher placement). If wall sconces are used in a hallway, they should generally be spaced about 8 to 10 feet apart.

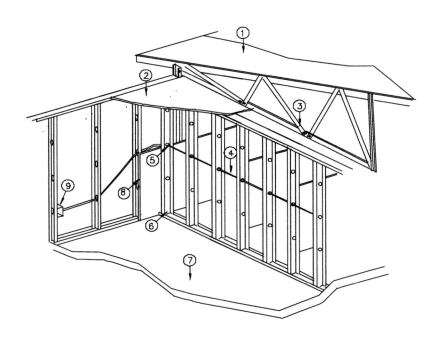

WIRING FROM EXTERIOR TO INTERIOR WALL

1. Roof sheathing.
2. ½" gypsum board ceiling to be installed prior to constructing interior walls.
3. Steel truss designed as an energy truss.
4. Electric conduit (romex).
5. Plastic grommet required at each stud Punch hole as required at 4' from floor.
6. Slammer stud - do not connect to track until gypsum board is installed on exterior wall.
7. Concrete slab, thermal mass. Use hard surface if possible.
8. Install ½" gypsum board on exterior wall. Long dimension to be parallel with floor. Notch at electric conduit as required.
9. Electric outlet box.

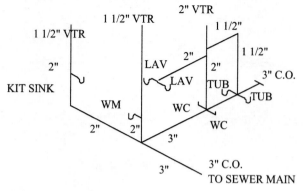

PLUMBING -ISO

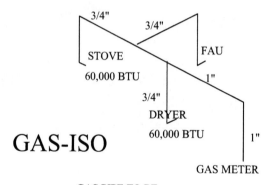

GAS-ISO

GAS PIPE TO BE
STD WEIGHT WROUGHT
IRON OR STEEL GALV. OR BLACK.

The installation of gas, water and sewer utilities should be done in a way that keeps penetrations of the ceiling at a minimum. Any penetrations through the ceiling should be caulked carefully to prevent convection air from escaping into the attic from the interior of the house.

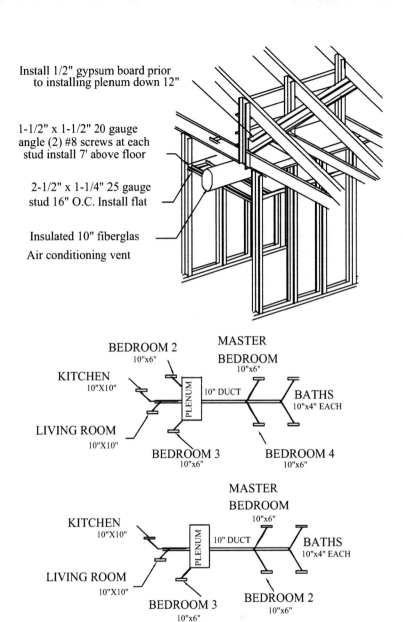

Install 1/2" gypsum board prior to installing plenum down 12"

1-1/2" x 1-1/2" 20 gauge angle (2) #8 screws at each stud install 7' above floor

2-1/2" x 1-1/4" 25 gauge stud 16" O.C. Install flat

Insulated 10" fiberglas

Air conditioning vent

BEDROOM 2
10"x6"

MASTER BEDROOM
10"x6"

KITCHEN
10"X10"

PLENUM

10" DUCT

BATHS
10"x4" EACH

LIVING ROOM
10"X10"

BEDROOM 3
10"x6"

BEDROOM 4
10"x6"

MASTER BEDROOM
10"x6"

KITCHEN
10"X10"

PLENUM

10" DUCT

BATHS
10"x4" EACH

LIVING ROOM
10"X10"

BEDROOM 3
10"x6"

BEDROOM 2
10"x6"

AIR CONDITIONING CONDUIT IN A SOFFIT

Chapter Fourteen
FOAMED CEMENT EXTERIOR WALLS

Increased indoor comfort levels
Heavy weight materials can smooth out indoor temperature swings and make use of solar gain without causing overheating. By using the mass of the insulated formed concrete exterior wall along with the mass of an insulated slab, the entire mass of materials stays at a more constant temperature. This slows indoor temperature changes throughout the day and night. The improved comfort is particularly noticeable in the summer as the exterior temperature increases and provides a reduction of drafts in the winter. The thermal mass also reduces heating and cooling demands in the same manner as an adobe or solid masonry dwelling, but with the obvious added advantage of the closed cell insulative structure of the foamed cement.

Reduction of sound levels
Knudsen and Harris (V.O. Knudsen and C.M. Harris) "Acoustical Designing in Architecture," presented a chart representing the average relationship between sound transmission loss and the weight of the barrier, published in the November, 1956 issue of American Concrete Institute. This chart shows clearly the decreasing value of wall weight affecting sound transmission. While the first 15 pounds per square foot offers a transmission loss of 40 decibels, the next 15 pounds increased the loss only by another five decibels.

Insulating steel framed walls with 6-inch blocks of foamed concrete weighing about 12 pounds per square foot and with ½-inch gypsum board, offers a transmission loss of approximately 39 decibels. This would reduce the noise from an average busy street from 60 decibels to 21 decibels, the same noise level as a whisper four feet away.

One system I have used successfully and would recommend is OTW blocks manufactured by Burrell Mining Products, Inc. Its main office is located at 2400 Leechburg Road, New Kensington, Pa. 15068, Phone 1-800-541-1575.

The blocks are composed of Portland cement, polyester fibers, and fly-ash (a waste material, power plants alone produce more 70 million tons normally disposed of in land fills) all of which are nontoxic and will not support combustion. Manufacturing methods produce a closed cellular structure which is non-absorptive and impervious to air. Using this integral wall component with metal framing results in a highly thermal and acoustic insulated structure with substantially no air infiltration. The steel frame and foamed cement core is extremely fire, rot and termite resistant, as well as to other pests such as rodents.

The assembled foamed concrete wall system does not produce a completely rigid structure, but one that will "give" in response to forces. The wall system provides limited twisting and flexure of the framing members, and acts as a vibration damping element. The 6-inch block based on testing by Ram Tec. Laboratories indicates an R-value of 12.9.

Testing on this wall system was completed by Ram Tec Laboratories, Inc. (NERQA-293) to determine the fire rating of the wall system. With ½-inch gypsum board on one side, it passed the fire test for a one-hour wall. The test was repeated using 5/8-inch gypsum board and passed a two-hour fire test with the metal at 375 degrees (400 is permitted) and the foamed concrete at 130 degrees.

This system is comprised of 6-inch thick by 23½-inch wide and 16-inch high blocks of foamed cement inserted between back to back 6-inch tracks employed at 24 inches on center. The interior flange of the track provides an interior surface for affixation of drywall. The block can be easily scored to install the electrical wiring. Steel straps or shear panels are installed to resist the lateral loads in the plane of the roof and wall, considering the foamed cement as a nonstructural element.

By adding OTW foamed cement blocks as insulation to the construction of the model house and using the Energy Pro computer program authorized by the California Energy Commission to compute energy efficiency, the house calculated to be 25 percent above the standard.

The installation of the block into the track is actually quite simple, and as the men erecting the structure become familiar with the system, the cost should be comparable to construction with wood. Energy savings and additional benefits, makes this system a superior way to build a house or commercial structure.

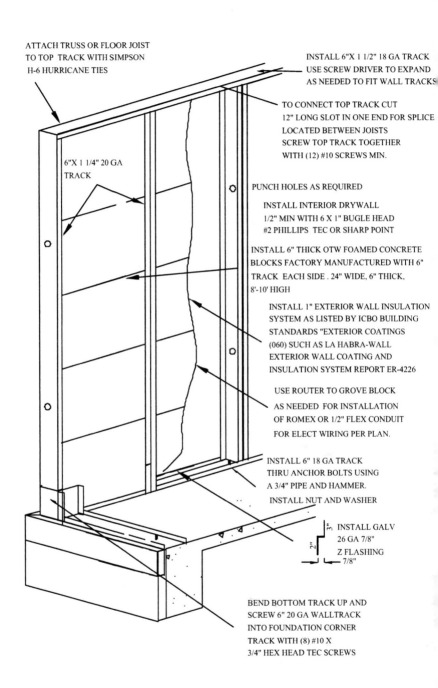

ATTACH TRUSS OR FLOOR JOIST
TO TOP TRACK WITH SIMPSON
H-6 HURRICANE TIES

INSTALL 6"X 1 1/2" 18 GA TRACK
USE SCREW DRIVER TO EXPAND
AS NEEDED TO FIT WALL TRACKS

TO CONNECT TOP TRACK CUT
12" LONG SLOT IN ONE END FOR SPLICE
LOCATED BETWEEN JOISTS
SCREW TOP TRACK TOGETHER
WITH (12) #10 SCREWS MIN.

6"X 1 1/4" 20 GA
TRACK

PUNCH HOLES AS REQUIRED

INSTALL INTERIOR DRYWALL
1/2" MIN WITH 6 X 1" BUGLE HEAD
#2 PHILLIPS TEC OR SHARP POINT

INSTALL 6" THICK OTW FOAMED CONCRETE
BLOCKS FACTORY MANUFACTURED WITH 6"
TRACK EACH SIDE . 24" WIDE, 6" THICK,
8'-10' HIGH

INSTALL 1" EXTERIOR WALL INSULATION
SYSTEM AS LISTED BY ICBO BUILDING
STANDARDS "EXTERIOR COATINGS
(060) SUCH AS LA HABRA-WALL
EXTERIOR WALL COATING AND
INSULATION SYSTEM REPORT ER-4226

USE ROUTER TO GROVE BLOCK
AS NEEDED FOR INSTALLATION
OF ROMEX OR 1/2" FLEX CONDUIT
FOR ELECT WIRING PER PLAN.

INSTALL 6" 18 GA TRACK
THRU ANCHOR BOLTS USING
A 3/4" PIPE AND HAMMER.
INSTALL NUT AND WASHER

INSTALL GALV
26 GA 7/8"
Z FLASHING
7/8"

3"

2"

BEND BOTTOM TRACK UP AND
SCREW 6" 20 GA WALLTRACK
INTO FOUNDATION CORNER
TRACK WITH (8) #10 X
3/4" HEX HEAD TEC SCREWS

TYPICAL OTW INSULATED WALL SECTION

115

INSTALLATION DETAILS FOR WINDOWS AND DOORS FOR OTW WALLS

The following is a step-by-step description of how to build headers with the OTW building system. The tools required are inexpensive, safe and easy to use.

One of these houses was built by an all woman volunteer crew for Habitat for Humanity in five days.

STEP ONE

SCREW 6"X1 5/8"
16 GA GALV STUD
7 7/8" LONG
WITH MIN (5)#10
TEC SCREWS TO
WALL TRACK
ON EACH SIDE
OF OPENING AT
6'8" ABOVE
FLOOR FOR
WINDOW & AT
6'10" ABOVE
FLOOR FOR
DOORS OR PER
BLDG PLAN

INSTALL FULL LENGTH
6"X16 GA TRACK FOR OPENINGS

OTW BLOCK
23 1/2" WIDE

STEP TWO

ATTACH 8" 18 GA STUD
TO EACH SIDE OF
THE 6" STUD WITH
(5) #10 TEC SCREWS
GA OF HEADER STUD
VARIES PER PLAN

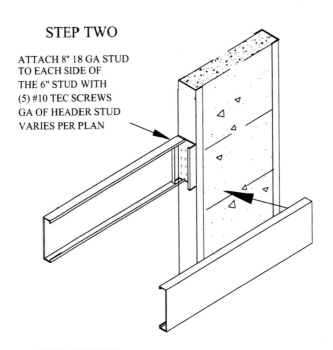

STEP THREE

FILL CAVITY BETWEEN
HEADER STUD W/INSULATION
INSTALL 6" 20GA TRACK
ON TOP AND BOTTOM
OF HEADER STUDS W/
#10 SCREWS AT 6" O.C.

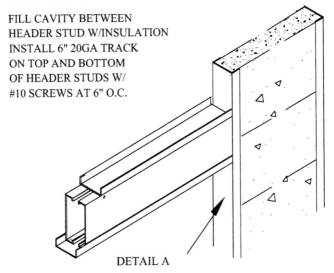

DETAIL A

TYPICAL HEADERS
ARE 4', 6' AND 8

STEP FOUR

CUT OTW BLOCKS INTO SECTIONS
AS REQUIRED WITH A HAND SAW AND
INSTALL IN TRACK OVER
HEADER STUDS, AND IN
BOTTOM TRACK AS REQ.

STEP FIVE

INSTALL 6"X 1 1/2" 18 GA
DEEP TRACK OVER TOP OF
OTW BLOCKS AND ATTACH
TO EACH STUD WITH (2)#
10 SCREWS, PAN HEAD ON
INTERIOR SIDE.

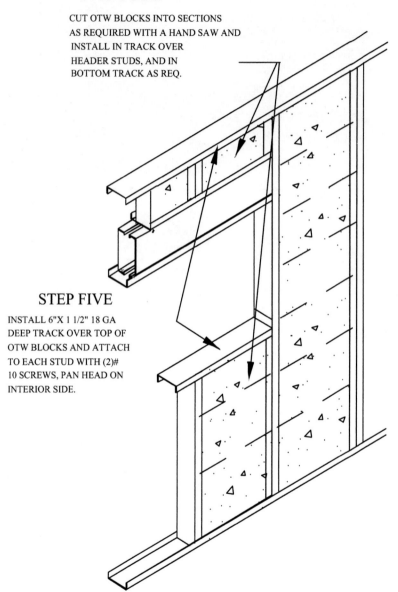

Window and Door headers

OTW installed wall sections

Women volunteers building a steel frame house using OTW insulating block.

Chapter Fifteen

ENERGY AUDIT

The energy calculation on the following pages was for a house located in the Coachella Valley in the California desert. In the design for the trusses, note the heel was raised 10 inches to make it an "energy truss," which means a full thickness of insulation is provided over the exterior wall section. Slab edge insulation was used in the foundation.

Even though this energy calculation is for a steel framed house, the calculations show it is 36.4 percent more energy efficient than the standard wood framed house. Adding OTW insulating blocks increased this to 53.2 percent.

The wheel below is based on a Manual J energy calculation. Note how the energy losses are now distributed.

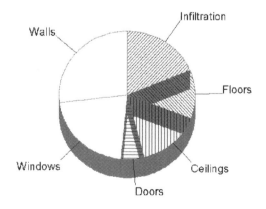

SAMPLE ENERGY CALCULATION USING RESCHECK

Note: In your calculations you may want to show windows and doors in the direction they actually face.

REScheck Software Version 3.7.3

Compliance Certificate

Project Title: AWARD WINNING HOUSE
Report Date: 08/28/06
Data filename: F:\\Untitled.rck

Energy Code:	**2000 IECC**
Location:	**Palm Springs, California**
Construction Type:	**Single Family**
Glazing Area Percentage:	**10%**
Heating Degree Days:	**985**

Construction Site:	Owner/Agent:	Designer/Contractor:
JOHNSON STREET	COACHELLA VALLEY HOUSING	JOHN HACKER
MECCA, CA	COALITION	CIVIL ENGINEER
	INDIO, CA	

Compliance: **Passes**   Maximum UA: **445**   Your Home UA: **283** --> **36.4% Better Than Code (UA)**
Maximum SHGC: **0.40** Your SHGC: **0.40**

Assembly	Gross Area or Perimeter	Cavity R-Value	Cont. R-Value	Glazing or Door U-Factor	UA
Ceiling 1: Raised or Energy Truss:	1320	38.0	0.0		33
Wall 1: Steel Frame, 24" o.c.:	1168	13.0	5.0		72
Window 1: Vinyl Frame:Double Pane: SHGC: 0.40	120			0.400	48
Door 1: Solid:	40			0.140	6
Floor 1: Slab-On-Grade:Heated: , Insulation Depth: 1.5'	146		5.0		124

Compliance Statement: The proposed building design described here is consistent with the building plans, specifications, and other calculations submitted with the permit application. The proposed building has been designed to meet the 2000 IECC requirements in REScheck Version 3.7.3 and to comply with the mandatory requirements listed in the REScheck Inspection Checklist.

_____   _____   _____

Builder/Designer   Company Name   Date

121

REScheck Software Version 3.7.3
Inspection Checklist

Date: 08/28/06

Ceilings:

☐ Ceiling 1: Raised or Energy Truss, R-38.0 cavity insulation
Comments: _____

Above-Grade Walls:

☐ Wall 1: Steel Frame, 24" o.c., R-13.0 cavity + R-5.0 continuous insulation
Comments: _____

Windows:

☐ Window 1: Vinyl Frame:Double Pane, U-factor: 0.400
For windows without labeled U-factors, describe features:
#Panes _____ Frame Type _____ Thermal Break? _____ Yes _____ No
Comments: _____

Doors:

☐ Door 1: Solid, U-factor: 0.140
Comments: _____

Floors:

☐ Floor 1: Slab-On-Grade:Heated, 1.5' insulation depth, R-5.0 continuous insulation
Comments: _____
Slab insulation to extend down from the top of the slab to at least 1.5 ft. OR down to at least the bottom of the slab then
horizontally for a total distance of 1.5 ft.
Exterior insulation must have a rigid, opaque, weather-resistant protective covering that covers the exposed (above-grade)
insulation and extends at least 6 in. below grade.

Solar Heat Gain Coefficient:

☐ The area-weighted average Solar Heat Gain Coefficient (SHGC) of all glazing cannot exceed 0.4. SHGC values must be
determined in accordance with the NFRC test procedure or taken from the default table.

Air Leakage:

☐ Joints, penetrations, and all other such openings in the building envelope that are sources of air leakage must be sealed.
☐ Recessed lights must be 1) Type IC rated, or 2) installed inside an appropriate air-tight assembly with a 0.5" clearance from
combustible materials. If non-IC rated, the fixture must be installed with a 3" clearance from insulation.

Vapor Retarder:

☐ Required on the warm-in-winter side of all non-vented framed ceilings, walls, and floors.

Materials Identification:

☐ Materials and equipment must be installed in accordance with the manufacturer's installation instructions.
☐ Materials and equipment must be identified so that compliance can be determined.
☐ Manufacturer manuals for all installed heating and cooling equipment and service water heating equipment must be provided.
☐ Insulation R-values and glazing U-factors must be clearly marked on the building plans or specifications.

Duct Insulation:

☐ Ducts in unconditioned spaces must be insulated to R-5. Ducts outside the building must be insulated to R-8.0.

Duct Construction:

☐ All joints, seams, and connections must be securely fastened with welds, gaskets, mastics (adhesives), mastic-plus-embedded-fabric, or tapes. Tapes and mastics must be rated UL 181A or UL 181B.
Exception: Continuously welded and locking-type longitudinal joints and seams on ducts operating at less than 2 in. w.g. (500 Pa).

☐ The HVAC system must provide a means for balancing air and water systems.

Temperature Controls:

☐ Thermostats are required for each separate HVAC system. A manual or automatic means to partially restrict or shut off the heating and/or cooling input to each zone or floor shall be provided.

Service Water Heating:

☐ Water heaters with vertical pipe risers must have a heat trap on both the inlet and outlet unless the water heater has an integral heat trap or is part of a circulating system.

☐ Insulate circulating hot water pipes to the levels in Table 1.

Circulating Hot Water Systems:

☐ Insulate circulating hot water pipes to the levels in Table 1.

Swimming Pools:

☐ All heated swimming pools must have an on/off heater switch and require a cover unless over 20% of the heating energy is from non-depletable sources. Pool pumps require a time clock.

Heating and Cooling Piping Insulation:

☐ HVAC piping conveying fluids above 105 degrees F or chilled fluids below 55 degrees F must be insulated to the levels in Table 2.

Table 1: *Minimum Insulation Thickness for Circulating Hot Water Pipes*

| | Insulation Thickness in Inches by Pipe Sizes | | | |
| | Non-Circulating Runouts | | Circulating Mains and Runouts | |
Heated Water Temperature (°F)	Up to 1"	Up to 1.25"	1.5" to 2.0"	Over 2"
170-180	0.5	1.0	1.5	2.0
140-169	0.5	0.5	1.0	1.5
100-139	0.5	0.5	0.5	1.0

Table 2: *Minimum Insulation Thickness for HVAC Pipes*

| Piping System Types | Fluid Temp. Range(°F) | Insulation Thickness in Inches by Pipe Sizes | | | |
		2" Runouts	1" and Less	1.25" to 2.0"	2.5" to 4"
Heating Systems					
Low Pressure/Temperature	201-250	1.0	1.5	1.5	2.0
Low Temperature	120-200	0.5	1.0	1.0	1.5
Steam Condensate (for feed water)	Any	1.0	1.0	1.5	2.0
Cooling Systems					
Chilled Water, Refrigerant and	40-55	0.5	0.5	0.75	1.0
Brine	Below 40	1.0	1.0	1.5	1.5

NOTES TO FIELD: (Building Department Use Only)

123

Chapter Sixteen

CONCLUSION

We are all faced with the consequences of global warming and it is up to each one of us to do our part in reducing the amount of carbon dioxide that is emitted into the atmosphere.

As we have outlined in the book, there are several things we can do to make our existing homes more energy efficient, save money and reduce pollution.

In review, to make your existing house more energy efficient, consider the following suggestions (which apply primarily to cooling your house, but will also help when heating it).

Number one: If you have a concrete slab for flooring, use it as a heat sink. Take advantage of the heat or cooling in the ground under the house by insulating the edge of the slab and using hard surfaces such as tile or laminated wood flooring.

Number two: Install solar screens on the windows to block the entry of radiant heat. Use retractable screens, which can be raised to allow winter sun to warm the slab, thus using it as thermal mass to store heat. If you live in a hot climate, window tinting is a good option.

Number three: Test your ducts for leakage and add additional insulation to your ducts if they are located in the attic.

Number four: Install power vents in the attic.

Number five: Install a radiant barrier to reflect heat away from the attic. This can be an option if power vents are impractical to install.

Number six: If you have a flat roof, consider coating it with a white elastomeric coating surface. This coating can reflect up to 90 percent of the heat from the sun. When installed on a hot black roof, a reflective roof coating keeps the roof from absorbing the heat and transmitting it into the building. Virtually any roof type can be restored such as gravel built up roofing, metal roofing, modified bitumen, polyurethane foam, and smooth built up roofing.

Number seven: Add insulation to your ceiling. If you have a flat roof, consider adding spray-on polyurethane foam to the roof. Benefits include reduced utility costs, increased structural strength and reduced air and water infiltration.

Number eight. In an older home a great deal of energy is lost due to gaps and opening around windows and doors. With a caulking gun fill in these gaps. Add gaskets to all your exterior wall plugs.

Number nine. If you intend to continue using your fireplace, consider installing a new fire box in place of the brick one. You can keep the beautiful look of your wood burning fireplace with the added cleanliness, energy efficiency and convenience of gas with a Gas Insert. Properly installed EPA certified wood stove and fireplace inserts burn wood efficiently, more safely, and heat your home effectively with much less smoke. In fact, you should see only a thin wisp of steam coming from your chimney.

The model home that is described in this book is tightly sealed for increased comfort and lower energy costs. The walls and ceiling are installed in a manner that makes a continuous air barrier, with tight doors and windows. In such a relatively small, tightly sealed house the pressure inside would overcome chimney draft and smoke would not be drawn out of the fire box. A wood burning fireplace is not recommended for this type of house.

HOME ENERGY EFFICIENCY IMPROVEMENT TAX CREDITS

Consumers who purchase and install specific products such as energy efficient windows, insulation, doors, roofs, and heating and cooling equipment can receive a tax credit of up to $500 beginning in January 2006.

The EPACT also provides a credit equal to 30 percent of qualifying expenditures for purchasing qualified photovoltaic property and solar water heating property used exclusively for purposes other than heating swimming pools and hot tubs. The credit does not exceed $2000.

Improvements must be installed in or on the taxpayer's principal residence in the United States. Home improvement tax credits apply for improvements made between January 1, 2006 and December 31, 2007.

Some consumers will also be eligible for utility or state rebates, as well as state tax incentives for energy efficient homes.

ABOUT TAX CREDITS

A tax credit is generally more valuable than an equivalent tax deduction because a tax credit reduces tax dollar-for-dollar, while a deduction only removes a percentage of the tax that is owed. Beginning in tax year 2006, consumers will be able to itemize purchases on their federal income tax form, which will lower the total amount of tax they owe the government.

A tax credit is available for the manufacturer of energy efficient dishwashers, clothes washers, and refrigerators. Credits vary depending on the efficiency of the unit. This is effective for appliances manufactured in 2006 and 2007.

Below is a table of anticipated tax savings and for energy efficient home improvements (as of November 2005): Tax Credit Specification to meet 2000 IECC & Amendments or Energy Star qualified.

Product	Tax Credit	
Windows, skylights	10% of cost not to exceed	$200
Exterior doors	10% of cost not to exceed	$500
Metal Roofs	10% of cost not to exceed	$500
Insulation	10% of cost not to exceed	$500
Central AC*		$300
Water Heater*		$300

* Central Air, such as air source heat pumps, geothermal heat pumps or split systems, must meet SEER/EER requirements.

* Water heaters must have an energy factor of 0.80 and electric heat pump water heaters must have an energy factor of 2.0.

Solar Electric systems and solar water heating systems should be evaluated closely before you consider installing them. A typical solar residential installation producing about 3.3 kWh costs about $30,000, with California and Federal rebates of about $10,000. The final cost to the home owner would be about $20,000.

It is estimated that the system will produce about 6,500 kWh per year. Payments at 6 percent interest on $20,000 over the projected 20 year life of the system would be about $143 per month or 27 cents per KWh. However it would take an acre of forest to absorb the amount of carbon dioxide emissions that this system eliminates from going out into the atmosphere.

Twenty-five years ago many solar water heaters were installed in various subdivisions to take advantage of credits. Now it is reported that some of these systems are failing. The cost of replacing and/or repairing solar water heaters can run into thousands of dollars. As a result, most home owners are installing standard gas units in their place costing about $400.

IN CONCLUSION

Construction plans for these homes have been made available free by my office for many years to non-profit organizations such as Habitat for Humanity, Building Horizons, and Boys and Girls Club of the Coachella Valley.

The homes are 1320 square feet in size and have proved to be energy efficient and very livable for a large family. Many families today feel that a livable home must be over 2000 square feet, but smaller energy efficient houses make good sense. We are faced with the effects of global warming and hear warnings of future shortages of electricity and natural gas with higher costs. These homes use less energy to cool and are comparatively inexpensive to build.

After your plans are drawn, make a take-off list for the steel studs and tracks you'll need. This can be done by making 10-scale drawings of each truss and each wall section separately and measuring each piece carefully. If you are careful, you should be able to assemble the frame with a minimum of problems and little cutting in the field.

Be aware of various sizes of studs. In the model house we used 3 ½"and 4" thick studs on the exterior wall to eliminate the hump where shear walls are installed. You may use 3 5/8" thick studs for the truss construction and at other locations.

Submit this cut list to your steel stud supplier who will be listed in the yellow pages under Building Materials.

I would recommend that you obtain sub-contractors for the concrete, air-conditioning, plumbing, electrical, plastering and finishing the gypsum board. Local homeowners providing "sweat equity" as a down payment for Coachella Valley Housing Coalition were limited to working on the framing and roof sheathing. If you are familiar with construction you may be able to install the outside lath, insulation, and gypsum board.

John H. Hacker, P.E., has designed buildings for more than 50 years. His steel framed designs have included convention centers, wineries, churches, and residential homes in the United States, Canada, Mexico, El Salvador, Guatemala, and Thailand.

He received the angel award from Oprah on her program for his volunteer work in designing homes for Habitat for Humanity.

He is also the author of the book, "LAUGHING AT GROWING OLD," a humorous book about grandchildren, marriage, doctor visits and other aspects of aging.

ORDER FORM

Order additional copies of" *Be Cool Despite Global Warming"* for loved ones, friends, and colleagues.

Call 760-340-4517 to order by credit card.

Or copy and mail this form and check payable to: I-Form Ink Publishing, Inc., 41-921 Beacon Hill, Suite A, Palm Desert, CA 92211.

Name: _____

Address: _____

City, State, Zip: _____

_____copies at $9.95 each   _____

Shipping $2.00 for first book, $1.00 each additional   _____

California Residents add $.77 tax per book   _____

                                     Total   _____

Payment: _____Check _____MasterCard or Visa

Card #_____

Exp. Date_____ Signature_____

Allow 15 days for delivery. Books can also be ordered on Amazon.com. or from your local book store.